# Civil engineering project procedure in the EC

# Civil engineering project procedure in the EC

Proceedings of the conference organized by the Institution of Civil Engineers and held at Heathrow on 24–25 January 1991

 Thomas Telford, London

Conference organized by the Institution of Civil Engineers

Organizing Committee: P.A. Cox (Chairman), M.W. Abrahamson, N.M.L. Barnes, D.J.O. Ferry, S.N. Mustow, D.E. Neale

Published on behalf of the Institution of Civil Engineers by Thomas Telford Ltd, Thomas Telford House, 1 Heron Quay. London E14 4JD.

Printed and bound in Great Britain by Redwood Press Limited, Melksham, Wiltshire

# Contents

**The future**

# A statistical introduction

Whether or not to take your business across frontiers may depend not only on your understanding of the business rules of the new country, but also on the size of the local market. The tables and histograms that follow compare the countries of the EC and Scandinavia in terms of size, construction output and some aspects of transport infrastructure.

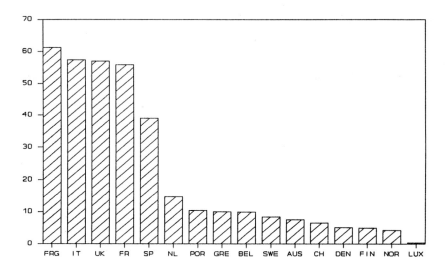

**Fig. 1.  Population (1988): millions**

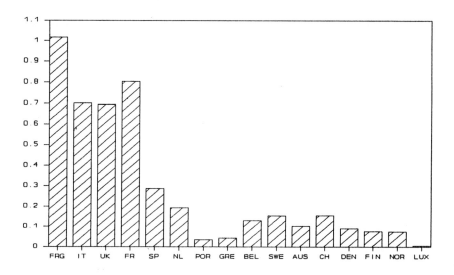

**Fig. 2.  GDP (1988): ECU x $10^{-12}$**

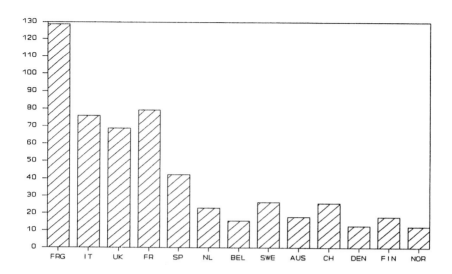

Fig. 3.   Construction output (1988): ECU x $10^{-6}$

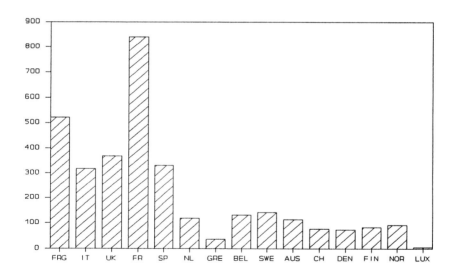

Fig. 4.   Road/rail length (1986-1988): km x $10^{-3}$

| | Area (km²) | Population (millions) 1988 | GDP (million ECU) 1988 | Road Length (km) 1988 | Motorway Length (km) 1988 | Railway Length (km) 1986 | Electrified Railway Length (km) 1986 | Construction Output (thousand ECU) 1989 | Road/Rail Length (km) 1986/88 |
|---|---|---|---|---|---|---|---|---|---|
| West Germany | 248577 | 61.20 | 1017451 | 493590 | 8618 | 27490 | 11433 | 128700 | 521080 |
| Italy | 301268 | 57.44 | 701789 | 301846 | 5997 | 16183 | 8936 | 76100 | 318029 |
| United Kingdom | 244100 | 57.08 | 695453 | 352292 | 2981 | 17038 | 4017 | 68730 | 369330 |
| France | 551500 | 55.87 | 804068 | 805070 | 6750 | 34665 | 11549 | 79240 | 839735 |
| Spain | 504782 | 39.05 | 287280 | 318022 | 2142 | 12721 | 6208 | 42270 | 330743 |
| Netherlands | 40844 | 14.76 | 193304 | 115305 | 2060 | 2817 | 1841 | 23030 | 118122 |
| Portugal | 92389 | 10.41 | 34434 | N/A | 238 | 3607 | 461 | N/A | N/A |
| Greece | 131990 | 10.01 | 44442 | 34492 | 92 | 2461 | 0 | N/A | 36953 |
| Belgium | 30514 | 9.92 | 130265 | 128319 | 1567 | 3691 | 2004 | 15700 | 132010 |
| Sweden | 440945 | 8.44 | 153570 | 131048 | 999 | 11700 | 7500 | 26320 | 142748 |
| Austria | 83853 | 7.60 | 101925 | 107099 | 1405 | 6400 | 3000 | 17930 | 113499 |
| Switzerland | 41293 | 6.51 | 155163 | 71055 | 1486 | 5100 | 5100 | 25600 | 76155 |
| Denmark | 43077 | 5.13 | 91056 | 70666 | 599 | 2471 | 199 | 12660 | 73137 |
| Finland | 338127 | 4.95 | 76475 | 76509 | 214 | 5900 | 1500 | 18000 | 82409 |
| Norway | 323895 | 4.20 | 75553 | 87603 | 74 | 4200 | 2400 | 12300 | 91803 |
| Luxemburg | 2586 | 0.37 | 5766 | 5085 | 75 | 270 | 162 | N/A | 5355 |

**Table 1  In descending order by population**

| | Area (km²) | Population (millions) 1988 | GDP (million ECU) 1988 | Road Length (km) 1988 | Motorway Length (km) 1988 | Railway Length (km) 1986 | Electrified Railway Length (km) 1986 | Construction Output (thousand ECU) 1989 | Road/Rail Length (km) 1986/88 |
|---|---|---|---|---|---|---|---|---|---|
| West Germany | 248577 | 61.20 | 1017451 | 493590 | 8618 | 27490 | 11433 | 128700 | 521080 |
| France | 551500 | 55.87 | 804068 | 805070 | 6750 | 34665 | 11549 | 79240 | 839735 |
| Italy | 301268 | 57.44 | 701789 | 301846 | 5997 | 16183 | 8936 | 76100 | 318029 |
| United Kingdom | 244100 | 57.08 | 695453 | 352292 | 2981 | 17038 | 4017 | 68730 | 369330 |
| Spain | 504782 | 39.05 | 287280 | 318022 | 2142 | 12721 | 6208 | 42270 | 330743 |
| Netherlands | 40844 | 14.76 | 193304 | 115305 | 2060 | 2817 | 1841 | 23030 | 118122 |
| Switzerland | 41293 | 6.51 | 155163 | 71055 | 1486 | 5100 | 5100 | 25600 | 76155 |
| Sweden | 440945 | 8.44 | 153570 | 131048 | 999 | 11700 | 7500 | 26320 | 142748 |
| Belgium | 30514 | 9.92 | 130265 | 128319 | 1567 | 3691 | 2004 | 15700 | 132010 |
| Austria | 83853 | 7.60 | 101925 | 107099 | 1405 | 6400 | 3000 | 17930 | 113499 |
| Denmark | 43077 | 5.13 | 91056 | 70666 | 599 | 2471 | 199 | 12660 | 73137 |
| Finland | 338127 | 4.95 | 76475 | 76509 | 214 | 5900 | 1500 | 18000 | 82409 |
| Norway | 322895 | 4.20 | 75553 | 87603 | 74 | 4200 | 2400 | 12300 | 91803 |
| Greece | 131990 | 10.01 | 44442 | 34492 | 92 | 2461 | 0 | N/A | 36953 |
| Portugal | 92389 | 10.41 | 34434 | N/A | 238 | 3607 | 461 | N/A | N/A |
| Luxemburg | 2586 | 0.37 | 5766 | 5085 | 75 | 270 | 162 | N/A | 5355 |

Table 2  In descending order by GDP

# 2. Risk sharing in contracts

M. BARNES, BSc(Eng), PhD, FICE, FAPM, Partner, Coopers and Lybrand
Deloitte

SYNOPSIS. The allocation of risk between the project owner and the contractor is established by the contract between them. Different forms of contract allocate the risk differently and can lead to very different outcomes for both parties. In this paper, the principles of contractual risk allocation are set down and the various forms of contract available are reviewed in terms of risk allocation and its effects. European practice and new developments in standard forms of contract designed to allocate risk more purposefully and effectively are discussed.

INTRODUCTION

1. The science of "risk analysis" as applied to construction and engineering contracts has been developed by researchers, mainly in the United States, over a number of years. The first work which showed that aspects of the science could be applied to contracts was carried out by Erikson (ref. 1). It is a quite different subject from "risk management", the name usually now given to the narrower subject of making insurance decisions according to an enfolding rationale.

2. The proposition which is the subject of this paper is that the subset of the science of "risk analysis" which is "risk allocation in contracts" can now be applied as a powerful method of assessing the effectiveness of different forms of contract and as an aid to designing new and significantly improved forms of contract. In particular, it enables the merits of different contracting practices used in the various European countries to be compared using a consistent set of criteria.

3. As a starting point, the basic concepts of risk allocation are set out using a simple illustration.

## AN ILLUSTRATION OF THE BASICS OF RISK ALLOCATION

4. Everything which people do is affected by uncertainty. There are two types of uncertainty, things which may or may not happen and things which are certain to happen but about which something is uncertain.

5. If one person begins to build a structure unaided and for himself, he has uncertainties of the first type such as the risk of falling off the structure and of the second type such as the risk of it taking five days to lay the bricks instead of two. He carries all these risks himself except those which he has chosen to cover by insurance.

6. If instead of for himself, the person is building the structure for a client, the builder may carry all, some or none of the risks which flow from the uncertainties, the others being carried by the client.

7. The one person builder could have agreed with his client that his payment will not be varied in any circumstances and that he will pay full compensation to the client if the structure is finished late or is at any time revealed to be imperfect in any way.

8. Alternatively, the contractor may have agreed with his client that he will be paid all his expenses, an amount for every hour of his time applied to the task and full compensation for any harmful effect which results from carrying out the task. In both cases, the risk carrier may insure himself to cover those risks which he chooses to and for which he can buy insurance at an acceptable cost.

9. If the contractor carries all the risks, he is very powerfully motivated to build the structure on time, without imperfections and efficiently. If prudent, he will have included a risk allowance in his price for the work which will cover the cost of the incidence of the risk events which is likely to materialise.

10. If the client carries all the risks, the contractor is motivated to take as long as possible over the work and has no motive to avoid or correct imperfections in it. There is no need for a risk allowance in his price.

11. This simple example and comparison introduces the basic issues which must be considered in allocating risks associated with construction projects. The example assumes only a client, a contractor, an agreement between them, a construction task, risks or uncertainties which affect the task and the availability of insurance.

12. The example demonstrates that the effect of the issues depends heavily upon the choice or design of the contract between the client and the contractor and, specifically, upon how the risks are allocated.

13. It also shows that the issues can be expressed without mentioning the law, the professional practices or the provisions of the conventional construction contracts which apply to a particular sector of the construction industry or to the industry of a particular country. It follows that the issues are common and that they underly the differing practices in different nations.

14. This is the starting point of this paper. It leads to consideration of the principles of effective risk allocation in construction contracts, how they are applied differently across Europe and how they might be used as the basis for harmonisation of contracting practice across Europe.

## THE PRINCIPLES OF RISK ALLOCATION
15. It is not difficult to make a very long list of the risks which may impact on a construction project. It is a list of all the uncertain causes which would have an effect upon the outcome of the project. The outcome is the result, the completion date actually achieved, the actual cost incurred and the actual quality and performance of the finished building or structure.

16. This list includes the high impact, low probability risks such as the risk of fire destroying the half built structure and the low impact, high probability risks such as the risk of the productivity of an excavator being 10% less than expected. Every contract provides for each of the risks to be allocated either to the client or to the contractor.

17. In all European systems, the risk allocation described in the particular contract is not the complete risk allocation statement. It may be qualified or even augmented by the law of the country. It may be qualified simply by the language of the country. For example, a contract in English may include words to this effect : "If event A happens, the client will pay the contractor any additional cost which the

event causes". Such words allocate the risk of event A to the client. If such words are not included, the risk is allocated to the contractor as clearly as if the fact had been stated in words in the contract. Consequently, contracts in English usually state which risks are to be allocated to the client, leaving all other risks allocated to the contractor.

18. This is not as unfair as it may seem, as the total amount of risk derives mainly from a relatively small number of the larger risks. For example, it has been estimated that the eight largest risks will usually account for as much as 90% of the total (ref. 2). If these eight were to be allocated to the client and the contract said nothing about allocation of any others, the contractor would only be carrying 10% of the total risk.

19. Risk allocation affects the behaviour of the parties to a contract because it affects their motivation. It follows that the best contractual risk allocation for the client is the one which motivates the contractor to try to achieve the client's objectives for the project - usually some combination of cost, time and performance of the completed project in use. The client's motives vary substantially from one project to another. The performance objective is most often dominant but is frequently supplanted by time, less often by cost.

20. The best risk allocation for the contractor is the one which motivates the client to try to achieve the contractor's objectives for the project. The contractor's objectives do not vary much from one project to another and, in market economy countries, are dominated by the profit motive. Again, these considerations are independent of the legal system and professional practices of each country.

21. An important aspect of the science of risk allocation is the answer it offers to the simple question of which party should carry a particular risk. The best answer seems to be that risks which the contractor can assess better than the client should be allocated to the contractor, others should be allocated to the client. Assessing a risk means both constraining its impact and forecasting the consequences of its impact.

22. For example, this answer leads to allocating the risk of bad weather to the contractor. He knows more than the client about how to protect construction activities from bad weather and more about the likely cost of bad weather effects against which he cannot protect. Another example is the risk of inflation. Neither the Contractor nor the

Client can control the rate of inflation and neither is likely to be better than the other at forecastingw what it will be. The risk of inflation should, therefore, be carried by the client.

23. Because it can be justified in more than one way, this principle of risk allocation is probably reasonably robust. It is claimed that contractors are typically risk averse and that clients are typically risk neutral (refs. 1 and 2). If this is true, the client achieves a marginal economy if, other things being equal, a risk is allocated to him. This is one reason why the basic rule of risk allocation leaves risks over which neither party has influence to the client.

24. Another principle which has significant benefit in practical application concerns the sizes of individual risks and of the size of the resulting total risk carried by each party. Risks do not add together arithmetically. They add according to the square root of the sum of the squares of each individual risk. This is the effect of the central limit theorem of statistics. The effect is well known to non-statisticians in English colloquial language as the swings and roundabouts effect.

25. In practice this means that the size of the total risk is heavily influenced by the size of the single largest risk and totally dominated by the sizes of the small group comprising the larger risks. If the largest risk can be shrunk or removed, it has a major beneficial effect. For example, this phenomenon makes it possible for the client to actually save money by doing some extra site investigation before inviting tenders for a tunnelling contract. This shrinks the largest single risk, that of encountering unforeseen ground conditions.

26. Perhaps surprisingly, if the risk of unforeseen ground conditions has been shrunk so much by site investigation that it is no longer amongst the larger risks, it can safely be carried by the contractor. It then has little impact on the size of his total risk. Contractors should not regard being asked to carry the risk of unforeseen ground conditions as a major assault on their commercial rights if it is only done when, on a particular project, this risk is not in the dominant group.

27. A method of limiting an individual risk is to specify in the contract that it is to be carried by the contractor within a stated limit and by the client if it goes beyond the limit. Unforeseen ground conditions clauses in U K contracts are usually of this type and contracts in the Netherlands have similar provisions.

28. Unfortunately, it is very difficult to define the limit clearly in ordinary language and many disputes arise when the circumstances actually experienced are near the risk transfer limits so defined. U K contracts define the limit of contractor's risk for unforeseen ground conditions using words like "conditions which he could reasonably have foreseen".

29. A statistical test would be more precise in principle but in practice is difficult if not impossible to establish. The adverse ground conditions which occur in one case out of ten would probabaly be a reasonable limit, but nobody has yet been able to set down a way of defining such a probability in sufficiently practical and argument-free terms.

30. The risk of bad weather is more amenable to this treatment. The as yet unpublished New Engineering Contract being prepared by a team headed by the author for the Institution of Civil Engineers has a risk transfer limit for bad weather expressed in statistical terms.

31. It is noteworthy that contracts used in Denmark have the lowest possible threshold of risk transfer to the client in both these areas. The contractor is compensated for virtually all interruptions of work due to bad weather and for all additional costs which are caused by ground conditions worse than those indicated in the site investigation information supplied to tenderers.

32. An important over-riding principle of risk allocation concerns the size of the total risk left to be carried by the contractor. Any standard or special form of contract can be analysed so that each risk on the long list referred to earlier can be categorised as allocated to the client, the contractor, an insurer or as shared by means of a risk transfer limit. Much commentary on standard forms and much reaction to them from contractors particularly centers around the allocation of risk in this way. However, it is the total magnitude of the risks allocated to him which matters most to the contractor, not how many or which of the risks on this list are allocated to him.

33. In competitively tendered construction contracts in the U K, the total cost risk carried by the contractor has a standard deviation normally between 5% and 10% In other words, a very good estimator will forecast the actual cost within 5% in two cases out of three and a rather bad estimator will get within 10% in two cases out of three. These variances are those which stem from the uncertainties due to the risks placed on the contractor by the contract.

34. If conditions of contract are used which increase the total risk carried by the contractor much beyond these rough figures, the probability of the lowest tenderer being the one who has most grossly under estimated the risks becomes high. If standard conditions consistently place large total risk on the contractor, the consistent result is that work goes to the optimists and the ignorant instead of to the foresighted and efficient.

35. In this situation, contractors become more motivated to pursue extra payment to recover from contracts awarded at prices which turn out to be low than to pursue efficiency in order to be able to submit low tenders. It is tempting to conclude that the growth of the pursuit of claims for extra payment in th U K construction industry is at least in part due to this factor.

36. It is overwhelmingly important in comparing different forms of contract, when applied to particular projects, to consider the total collective magnitude of the risks to be carried by the contractor, not the length of the list of the risks he is to carry or which individual risks he is to carry.

37. To make this point by illustration, consider two projects to be carried out using the same conditions of contract. One is to a design which has been used many times before for a client whose requirements are stable. It is to be constructed on a site in a city where the access is easy and the ground conditions well known. The other is to a new design for a client who is likely to change his mind often and late. It is to be constructed on a remote, inacessible upland site in an area of dramatic but uncharted geology. The lists of risks to be carried by the contractor in each case are identical. The magnitude of the risk is entirely different.

38. It follows that the appropriateness of any standard form of contract, as regards allocation of risk, cannot be considered entirely in general terms. Its appropriateness must be considered in the light of the magnitude of the risks in the case of each project to which the contract might be applied.

39. A final factor affecting the principles of risk allocation is that of contractor reputation. In many countries it is the culture that repeat business for contractors depends upon treating the current client well. Contractors may be motivated to absorb risks which the contract says

they need not. Their reputation with the client is heightened or sustained so that the chance of getting further work from the same client is increased.

40. In the U K, the culture has developed over the last forty years that many contractors pursue payment in every way that the words of the contract could possibly be interpreted to allow. Any lowering of their reputation which this might cause does not appear to be seen as a problem. In other countries, pursuit of payment is seen as more harmful to reputation. Consequently, conditions of contract can allocate more risks to the contractor. The risk premiums for doing so are paid indirectly by the client in tender prices. In extremis, this practice can cost the client money. If kept within bounds, it must reduce cost if only by reducing the sizes of the teams of qunatity surveyors and claims experts otherwise required.

## RISK ALLOCATION IN DIFFERENT TYPES OF CONTRACT

41. In this section, the newer forms of contract are compared with traditional competitive tender contracts.

42. In European countries the level at which design work is undertaken by the contractor varies considerably. Linking design and construction within one contractor adds to the list of risks he carries but reduces the size of several risks on the list. Generally, in th U K and in other parts of Europe, design and build is seen by contractors as a lower risk form of contract than the conventional. It need not be a higher risk procedure for clients if they specify their requirements and choose their design and build contractors very carefully.

43. A device which can reduce the total contractor risk without shortening the list of contractor carried risks is the target or target cost contract. In its simplest form (as yet not widely used), the client and contractor share the differnce between actual total cost and forecast total cost. If they share this difference equally, the risk to the contractor is halved and an identity of motive between the client and the contractor is achieved. Theoretically elegant to the risk analyst and business man alike, the target form of contract does not appear to be gaining popularity anywhere in Europe. This is because of its administrative complexity which can easily prevent the motives theoretically implanted by the system being realised.

44. Management and construction management contracts have been extremely popular in the U K and the U S and also in mainland Europe in a slightly different form. The principle of these contracts is that the contractor carries none of the risks on the list. They are carried either by the client or by subcontractors. The risk frontier is moved from the client/contractor interface to the contractor/ subcontractor interface. Consequently, the risks are managed in a different way. Some of them can be shrunk significantly in the hands of a competent management contractor. Records in the U K building industry show that the system does reduce risk for the client when it is operated by contractors competent in its special skills. This is despite the fact that the subcontracts used with the system often place a very large total risk upon the subcontractors.

## A CONTRACT FOR EUROPE

45. The principles of risk allocation in construction contracts apply to any type of project carried out in any country and within any legal framework. The concept of a European standard form of contract must, at least as regards risk allocation, be theoretically sound. Unfortunately, it seems likely to be too difficult to achieve in practice, at least in the short term.

46. This is because working practices are currently too different from one country to another. A particular risk which contractors habitually take in one country may be regarded by contractors in another as the one which it is the very core of their commercial rights that the client must carry. The boundary between design and construction is by habit placed differently in different countries. To move it would require whole professions to alter their range of skill and knowledge. They will not see why they should, particularly if the change shrinks their scope significantly.

47. There is no doubt that a unified European contract could be developed and that the will to do so is in some hearts. The arguments for not doing so can be no stronger than those which lost the argument against national standard forms in earlier times. The New Engineering Contract referred to earlier must point the way towards such a contract without frontiers. It has been drafted on the basic and universal principles of risk allocation set out in this paper. It is in simple language which lends itself to unambiguous translation. It does accommodate all the types of contract currently available.

49. The European Commission is taking difficult steps to ensure that tendering for construction contracts will be unrestricted across national boundaries within a comparatively short time. This will achieve little if the reward for contractors able to tender in a different country is to have to work with a form of contract alien to their accumulated skills, commercial data and practices. There can be no real equality of opportunity if only contractors from the home country actually know how to carry out the contracts which have been newly opened to international competition. A real European standard form of contract is bound to come - but how soon?

## REFERENCES

1. ERIKSON C.A. Risk sharing in construction contracts. PhD thesis, University of Illinois, 1979

2. PORTER C.E. Risk allocation in construction contracts. MSc thesis, University of Manchester Institute of Science and Technology, 1981

# 3. The organisation of procurement

D. FERRY, PhD, FRICS, Research Manager, CIRIA

SYNOPSIS. Although the methods of procurement of extremely large construction projects tend to be internationalised, for the majority of projects national and regional practices are the norm. EC Directives will certainly have an effect on the opening up of public sector projects to greater competition within the community, but otherwise changes towards harmonization are likely to be slow.

INTRODUCTION

1. 'Procurement' is a word only recently encountered in the context of construction work, and, as is often the case with new usages, there is some variation in the exact meaning assigned to it by its users. In this paper the term is considered to include the total process of procuring such work, from the client's initial idea through to his occupying and operating the finished asset.

2. Unlike the manufacture and selling of construction materials and components, a substantial part of the actual construction of a civil engineering work must take place at the site, in whatever country or region that may be.

3. The component tasks of the construction procurement process can be itemised as follows:

(i) Inception

a Brief
b Financial assessment
c Planning requirements/environmental impact
d Decision on project management or other procurement method
e Decision on proceeding

(ii) Design

a Alternative conceptual designs
b Strategic development of chosen design
c Design of specialist works
d Financial implications of design(s)

e     Detailed development of design
f     Preparation of working drawings
g     Design of temporary works
h     Approval of contractor (& specialist) designs
i     Payment for design

(iii) Construction

a     Selection of procurement method
b     Selection of main or management contractor
c     Selection of works contractors
d     Determining works programme
e     Insurances, definition of liabilities, etc
f     Mobilisation of resources
g     Overall management and co-ordination
h     Management of works
i     Inspection and approval of works
j     Payment for management
k     Payment for works

(iv) Commissioning/Running

a     Testing of installations
b     Commissioning of works
c     Warranties and guarantees
d     Hand-over
e     Final payment to parties
f     Responsibility for running/maintenance

4.   Although these component tasks are common to most (if not all) construction projects throughout the world, the different countries and regions of Europe have evolved their own mechanisms for undertaking them, based in the first instance upon their historical legal and academic systems and business practices but modified to take account of developing professional and commercial roles during the 19th and 20th centuries.

5.   The parties to a project in the various countries, even though they may have similar names (e.g. engineer, architect, contractor), may therefore have acquired responsibility for quite different combinations of the above tasks.  To complicate the issue still further these may vary within different sectors of the industry (e.g. public works, commercial building) or in different regions of the country, and may be further undergoing change in the dynamic economic and political conditions of the last decade.

6.   One thing is however very clear.  Because construction was one of the earliest industries to become established on a major scale, and because it affects the environment of a locality more than any other industry, its practices have grown

up within a strong local tradition and may be enshrined in long-standing local, regional, or even national, legislation.

7. Traditional construction roles are therefore deeply embedded in the cultures of the countries concerned, and are going to take a long time to change. England and Scotland have been totally integrated within a single Union for almost two centuries, yet even today there are considerable divergences of practice (and of law) between the two countries. Similarly it is going to take some while for European normalisation to bring all national and regional practices into line.

8. Contractual systems and formalized procurement methods do little more than codify accepted practice, and depend for their effectiveness upon a wide measure of agreement about their procedures and fairness. Invariably they reflect the preoccupations of the nation - the traditional British obsession with accountability, for example, or the German liking for conformity.

9. As a general rule however the smaller a project the more likely it is that local customs will play a large part in its execution, and indeed that attempts to overthrow local custom may well lead to inefficiency, increased costs, and a generally unsatisfactory outcome. Conversely, the execution of megaprojects, even before 1992, is increasingly becoming internationalised and the arrangements under which a hundred-million pound project is procured would vary much less between, say, the UK and France or Italy than would a more modest scheme. This is largely because traditional and locally familiar means of procurement rarely lend themselves to schemes which are much larger, and more technically and managerially complex, than those for which they were developed.

10. Turning now to more specific matters, this paper is limited in its scope to the five large members of the European Community - the UK, France, Spain, Germany, and Italy, and is based upon the work carried out for CIRIA in preparing its reports on the construction industries of these countries.

11. Each of these countries has developed its own approaches to the complex problems of designing and procuring construction works. In most of them (though not in England) the regions have considerable autonomy and independence. Public construction budgets and the administration of private construction are governed from the Regional or Land capital, not from Paris, Madrid, or Bonn, and much of the power often resides at the subordinate level of government, the municipality. Procurement practices may therefore vary between regions. In Germany in particular only the largest firms operate outside their own Region, and this is only slightly less true in the other countries.

12. Harmonisation will also be made even more difficult by the fact that in some countries (particularly the more Southern European ones) what is supposed to happen according to the book, and what actually happens in practice, are two rather different things. Sometimes the carefully regulated industry

which exists on paper and the reality on site (especially away from the prestige projects in the capital) can bear little resemblance to one another, although as a rule the paperwork still has to be suitably completed.

13. Nevertheless the influence of the European Commission on public procurement policies in particular will be considerable. This is especially important to the civil engineering branch of the construction industry, since so much of its work is in the public or quasi-public sector and since in some countries (though not the UK) there is traditionally a fundamental difference between procurement practices in the public and private sectors. Although it may take some time for the Commission's edicts to be fully adhered to at local level, strict compliance is obviously going to be demanded for the substantial body of work funded in whole or part by the Commission.

14. But in general the European construction industries for a long time to come will continue to owe far more to their traditional regional development than to anything that comes out of Brussels.

DIFFERENCES BETWEEN UK AND CONTINENTAL PRACTICE

15. Although as has been said each country is different there are nevertheless a number of ways in which UK practice can be said to be at variance with that generally applicable on the continent.

16. Firstly, the importance of the UK professional consultant and the professional institutions, which latter by and large have no exact continental equivalents - most of their professional organisations are either trade or academic associations or purely registration bodies. Although in some countries the individual professional person has even more prestige than in Britain, there is not the same distinction between 'client-oriented' professional organisation and the commercial firm from which the client has to be protected. This obviously has an effect on the basis of contracts. And in general continental practitioners are not grouped into large non-commercial consulting organisations to the extent that they are here.

17. A second major difference is in the legal basis of construction. The UK , unlike many of the mainland countries, did not come under the influence of Napoleon and his codified legal system based on Roman law. Many of the issues which arise on a construction contract in continental Europe are embodied in the law of the land and there is no need to spell them out in the pitiless detail required by the British dependence on the law of contract underwritten by a rather nebulous common law. This particularly applies to considerations relating to responsibility for the fitness of the finished works, and the need in Britain to safeguard the client's interests in a situation where statute law does not do

so may partially account for the role of the professional already referred to.

18. In general however the execution of building works on the continent is more affected by legislation than is the case with infrastructure work, possibly because clients in the latter sector are usually competent technically.

19. A third difference between the UK and the continent is the adversarial attitude which even today governs British construction work - many projects, especially large ones, degenerate into a series of battles between the contractor and the client's advisors, between the sub-contractors and the main contractor, and between labour and employer. Mutual trust is traditionally absent.

20. Fourthly, the division of the construction industry into Building and Civil Engineering sectors staffed by almost entirely separate people, with their own traditions, relationships, and procedures, is much more noticeable in the UK than elsewhere. Perhaps associated with this the proportion of construction expenditure related to civil work is invariably higher in continental countries than in the UK, often markedly so.

21. And finally, the British construction industry is probably unique in Europe in the extent to which contractors have interested themselves in land and property, and have used land-dealing as a substantial contribution to their profitability.

22. Other differences which affect national and commercial life more generally, but also impinge upon construction procurement, concern the structure of firms and the role of the banks and other finance houses, two issues that are closely interlinked.

23. The family-controlled firm is still a common business structure on the continent, even for quite large organisations, and can lead to a greater pride in the firm's work both by management and, equally important, by the workforce who are far more likely to be long-term direct employees than in the UK.

24. Such firms have been enabled to survive and prosper by the attitude of the banks, who unlike their British counterparts do not see themselves primarily in the role of short-term moneylenders, but prefer to take a permanent stake in the firms that they finance. They are thus not necessarily looking for short-term results but for long-term prosperity, and avoid the need for the firm to seek outside equity with the concomitant need to be please the stock market and to be judged on immediate profitability. Regionalisation, of course, is another factor which encourages the existence of family firms with their roots in the community.

25. With the exception of a comparatively few very large firms most continental contractors are small - there is rarely any counterpart of the large number of medium-sized national contractors found in Britain. This trend is accentuated by the tradition of separate-trades contracts in most continental

INTRODUCTION

countries, and by the absence of property interests to swell
most contractors' portfolios.
    26.  Given the problems of language and local knowledge,
collaboration with local organisations is almost certainly a
better option for firms seeking to work in other EC countries
than competition, and indeed they will find it difficult to
break into the local market without such support.  The strength
of local loyalties and the required knowledge of local customs
and conditions means that, as already mentioned (para.11), even
continental firms do not always find it easy or profitable to
work in other regions of their own country.
    27.  After so many generalisations it is now time to look at
the more specific issues relating to each country

THE UNITED KINGDOM
    28.  Since so many delegates are from the UK it may be
convenient to consider this as the norm, and to then look at
divergencies in practice elsewhere.
    29.  The most usual, and traditional, procurement method is
on the basis of the appointment of a main contractor to carry
out the works to the designs prepared by, and under the
supervision of, the Engineer representing the client.  The
contractor's appointment is most often made as the result of
competitive tendering against the drawings and specification
supplied by the Engineer, and although his tender will be shown
as a lump sum the work itself will be measured as executed and
priced according to the rates inserted (by the contractor)
against the items in a bill of quantities supplied by the
Engineer.
    30.  The permanent works are normally designed in detail by
the Engineer and the contractor is not required to contribute
to the design process, although he will have more discretion in
the case of temporary works.  He will usually have control over
the timing and methods of carrying out the work under the
Engineers general approval and any overall programme laid down
by him; his responsibility for quality of the permanent works
is usually limited to doing what he is told.
    31.  The contractor may assign or sub-contract parts of the
work subject to the Engineer's approval - this practice is
tending to increase, though not on the scale now customary in
the Building sector of the industry.
    32.  The great bulk of Civil Engineering work is carried out
for clients in the public sector (or for recently privatised
ex-public sector organisations) who normally have qualified
professional engineers on their in-house staff.  To complicate
matters for other EC members the chief engineer of a local
authority is often called the County Surveyor or Borough
Surveyor although he is unlikely to be a surveyor by
profession.
    33.  The Engineer for the purposes of a project may either be
a member of the client's in-house staff or a consulting firm.
Some of these firms are very large, over 4000 staff perhaps,

22

and they are required to preserve a total independence from the contracting industry, and indeed from commerce generally. Firms of this nature acting as the prime movers in normal construction procurement are a feature of the UK system which makes it rather different to others in the EC.

34. The project is normally financed almost entirely by the client, who makes (usually monthly) stage payments to the contractor representing 90 -100% of the value of the work executed.

35. Other methods of procurement (such as target cost) are occasionally used, but the in-house or independent Engineer acting as an intermediary between the client and the contractor is an almost invariable feature of them. Design-and-construct is rarely encountered in civil engineering, although it is very common in process and petro-chemical engineering construction which in the UK at any rate is regarded as a different field.

36. Although many of the largest client bodies use their own forms of contract these are mostly based upon the Institution of Civil Engineers standard Form Of Contract (currently under revision). This Form and its derivatives emphasise the quasi-judicial role of the Engineer, who is expected to act impartially between the parties in making his decisions, even though he is employed and paid by one of them.

37. It will thus be seen that in UK practice the Engineer employed by the client is responsible for (or is responsible for advising the client on):

(i) Inception

All aspects a - e

(ii) Design

All aspects a - i except:

c Design of specialist works (where he may simply approve designs prepared by specialists)

g Design of temporary works (which may be done by the main contractor)

i Payment for design (since he is doing the design and will be paid by the client)

(iii) Construction

Four of aspects a - k only:

a Selection of procurement method
b Selection of main or management contractor
i Inspection and approval of works
k Payment for works

(iv) Commissioning/Running

All aspects except:

f     Responsibility for running/maintenance

38.   There is thus a very clear division between the execution of design and supervision on the one hand, and the actual construction process on the other, the two being linked by formal contractual relationships.

39.   A very recent development are projects where a scheme including its finance is got together by a consortium which would include contracting and investment interests.  These have not been widely enough adopted to enable generalisations to be made about the procurement methods involved, but it would be expected that the role of the independent engineer would be less central than it is in the traditional project.

40.   A final point to be made about the UK industry is the total separation between Building work (which comprises about 80% of the national construction programme, a much higher figure than in continental European countries) and Civil Engineering.  Although most large contracting organisations carry out both types of work the two activities are kept quite separate within the firm, with different staffs involved.  The Civil Engineering profession is little involved in building work, where the Architect fulfils many of the same roles, a completely different Standard Form of Contract (in which the ICE has no involvement) is used, the Bills of Quantities perform the usual function of the Specification, and the Structural Engineer works under the direction of the Architect.

41.   The UK Building scene differs more from normal continental practice than is the case with Civil Engineering.

FRANCE

42.   In France the profession of engineer is highly regarded on academic grounds, and it seems less necessary to protect it with organised professional structures similar to the British institutions.  A French engineer does not qualify in a particular branch of engineering, but develops a specialism as a work-skill.  One thus would not have, for instance, such a clear distinction between Civil and Structural engineers as exists in the UK.

43.   The whole demarcation between professionalism and commercialism in business is much more vague in France than in the UK, and the French seem to cope quite easily with situations which in a British context would be seen as giving rise to conflicts of interest.

44.   Thus the 'bureaux d'etudes techniques' (BET) which are approximate counterparts of the British consulting engineers office, though nominally acting independently, are often owned by contracting groups and always have a fairly commercial orientation.  As well as civil engineering and structural

engineering work they also tend to undertake most of the production design work, management, and financial assessment on Building projects (covering much of the work done in the UK by architects and quantity surveyors), though it is necessary to employ a registered architect on building works for the conceptual design and to obtain a building permit.

45. There are thus differences between building and civil engineering work, but these are not nearly so marked as in the UK and both the BET and to a lesser extent the contractors span both sectors in a way unknown in Britain, with advantages to both.

46. In civil engineering the BET does not determine detailed design to anything like the extent of their UK counterparts, and the contractors are expected to develop the BET's conceptual design themselves. Contracts are traditionally let separately for each trade, though general contracting is becoming more common (especially using consortia of trade contractors brought together for each project). Lump-sum tenders obtained in competition are preferred, though civil engineering works are often remeasured at completion because of the difficulty of determining the extent of work, particularly groundworks, in advance.

47. But the whole process seems to involve less confrontation and an easier settlement than is often the case in Britain. A defender of the British way of life might say that this is because French clients do not realise that they are being exploited by the heavily commercialised set-up. But a Frenchman might equally reply that he is more interested in getting on with the job than in arguing about it!

SPAIN

48. The Spanish situation has more in common with France than with Britain. There is a tendency for design bureaux not to be involved in supervision, and there are a larger number of traditional engineering consultancies (though these are sufficiently thin on the ground to be grouped with Management Consultants in their trade association).

49. But an additional complication is that the banks, which are heavily involved in industry, are involved also in design consultancies.

50. As in France the contractor is usually responsible for detail design, and on smaller projects for total design, and in law he bears most of the risk. The law makes quite a distinction between building projects, where an architect has to be involved, and civil works, and also between private and public sector work where different forms of contract are used. There is a mass of legislation governing the procurement of public work, allowing either an 'auction', where discounts are quoted off a priced bill of quantities, a lump sum competitive system where aspects other than the price can be taken into account, or straightforward negotiation. The legislation sets

out the conditions under which one or the other may be used, and the requirements which have to be observed.

51.   The bureaucratic and legislative complexities are so great that it is common for even Spanish firms to employ a special consultant whose job it is to guide them through this minefield.

## GERMANY

52.   In Germany there is much less distinction between building and civil engineering work than in the countries so far considered, the word 'bau' covering both.   Similarly the demarcation between architects and engineers is less important.

53.   The main distinctions made are between 'public works' and other work, although of course most civil engineering falls into the former category.   The construction industry is divided into major and secondary firms (the latter including most of the sub-contractors), belonging to different organisations and subject to different regulations.

54.   Consulting engineers are organised in a way more familiar to British eyes than in France and Spain.   A number of different tendering alternatives are laid down by law for public works, and it is advisable to follow these for private work also.   General contracting is common, but as is usual in continental Europe the contractor has more responsibility for design than in the UK, and far more responsibility at law for the adequacy of the finished work.

55.   The German industry is heavily legislated, but in general everybody understands the requirements and observes them.   This problem is eased to some extent by the practice, already mentioned (para.11), of firms working only within their own Land where they know the rules and the people.

## ITALY

56.   As is the case with Germany, in Italy the demarcation between engineers and architects is not so clearly defined as in the UK, France, and Spain, and in fact they are both covered by the same legislation regarding education and qualification.

57.   Even more than Britain, Italy has the problem of prosperous regions close to the rest of Europe, and increasing poverty and unemployment the further one moves towards the periphery.

58.   The Italians are probably more renowned for their engineering projects than for their present-day buildings, and there is a national pride in such things perhaps even greater than that which exists in France.

59.   Engineering consultancies exist much as in the UK, but with the usual continental tendency towards smaller firms exaggerated by legal problems facing large consultancies.   A feature of Italian procurement is the required appointment of a Director of Works for each project, who may or may not be the design consultant, and who has general responsibility for the fitness of the works (but not for final inspection and

certification which has to be done by an independent consultant).

60.   Italian procurement of public works is also characterised by public tendering with a very large number of tenderers usually involved, and partly because of this the settlement process tends to be more familiar to British eyes than is the case in the other countries considered, with substantial differences between low tender prices and considerably enhanced final accounts, and with considerable delays in final payment.

61.   But of all the countries considered Italy is the one where the differences between the official systems (both European Community and Italian domestic) and what actually happens in practice are greatest, and the warning about doing business in another country without local participation applies most strongly here.

GENERALLY

62.   It will be seen that although the Community is certainly moving towards harmonisation of procurement the process is unlikely to be rapid, and 1992 will mark an important step along the road rather than being a cataclysmic event.

# Discussion on Papers 2 and 3

R. BLAKEBROUGH, Costain Civil Engineering Ltd, Erith
Do British contractors take more risks than contractors from the more developed mainland European nations? If the answer is no, then who does? The basis of this question is that he who best judges risk is more likely to succeed than his competitors.

PROFESSOR D. BISHOP, Liability Task Force, c/o ICE, London
John Uff, QC, one of the two legal experts of the Liability Task Force, has long argued that 'a contract for Europe' would be one of the more practical and direct routes to harmonization. This could be attempted in stages, perhaps commencing with little more than headings to illustrate the scope and structure of a future harmonized contract. On this basis, the detail of clauses could be completed as experience and confidence allowed. Such an approach would enable a start to be made quickly without the delay inevitably entailed in drafting a complete contract acceptable to the industries in twelve member states.
The review of the liability of construction professionals (Professional Liability, HMSO, October 1989) included an analysis of the records of the Official Referees' Court. This demonstrated that the volume of litigation is small compared to the size of the industry and the opportunities for conflict. In the survey years there was roughly a 1/200 chance that a project would result in a writ being registered with the Official Referees' Court and a 1/2000 chance that a project would produce a dispute that would be decided by an official referee of claims circumstances notified to brokers: roughly 40% are settled by negotiation; 20% result in a visit. In the latter case, roughly 14% (of the total) result in a negotiated settlement.

J. E. WALLACE, Enco Civil Engineering Ltd, Slough
Mr Abrahamson knows only too well the risks that contractors accept in their own countries. Could he

comment on the bravery of continental contractors in
venturing into foreign lands? My own experience shows
that many continental European contractors have worked
on major projects in Ireland in joint ventures with my
company, whereas we have not yet ventured into Europe
even in joint venture.

Does Mr Abrahamson have any comments on the case of a
client looking for a fixed price to satisfy a financier
as to the final cost before a project commences?

G. HAWKER, London

Referring to Dr Ferry's statement (paragraph 61) that
differences between the official system and what
actually happens in practice are greatest in Italy, I
would cite a judgement of Mr Justice Donaldson (as he
then was) to the effect that in civil engineering
no-one ever bothered to read the Contract, but just got
on with the job unless disaster intervened, in which
case they flew to the Contract to see whether it could
help to put things right or at least dump the problem
in someone else's lap. I am curious to know to what
extent such an attitude prevailed in the countries of
Europe.

J. W. BARRACK, Mowlem Management Ltd, Twickenham

I would be interested to hear comments on the subject
of minimizing risk before looking at risk sharing: not
enough time is spent on risk reduction, and after all,
if a client has offloaded the risk he has not
necessarily achieved anything until his objectives are
achieved.

Is the power of lowest price as dominant in mainland
Europe as in the UK, particularly looking at the
current UK market, and coupling with risk where
contractors at very low margins are going to be looking
at ways of recovering their positions?

R. K. OLIVER, Walter Lawrence Management Ltd, Enfield

Dr Barnes refers to onerous subcontract conditions.
These are not necessarily introduced by the Managing
Contractor, but result from the imposition of
non-standard clauses by the Client.

D. FERRY, Paper 3

To Professor Bishop's contribution regarding the
liability of construction professionals I have nothing
to add.

Regarding Mr Hawker's point concerning the tendency
of parties only to resort to reading the contract when
trouble looms, in Continental Europe contracts are
generally less voluminous than in the UK, and many of
the matters, particularly those concerning liability
and the like, are embodied in legislation rather than

having to be spelt out individually in various contract forms. Therefore for both these reasons the practice to which Mr Hawker refers is less common on the Continent. Because legislation does not have to be relearned every time for each contract, people have a much better idea of their liabilities at the time when they are tendering.

With regard to Mr Barratt's point, lowest price is still the most usual way of awarding a contract on the Continent, but for various reasons partly to do with the financial structure of firms and the extent to which they are expected to finance the works during construction, there is less of a tendency to submit unrealistically low bids. An exception to this occurs in Italy where the practice of having enormously long tender lists for public projects does lead to the UK situation of unrealistic tenders and the attempts to recoup losses through the submission of claims.

# 4. Organisation of a construction operation in France

P. LALAURIE, Manager, OTH

SYNOPSIS    In France, the organisation of a construction operation is very different depending on whether the project is for a client in the public or the private sector.  I will make a separate analysis for each case, starting with the public sector.

## OPERATIONS DEPENDENT ON A PUBLIC AUTHORITY

### Definition
1.    Projects built by the following bodies are regulated by public contracts:
. the state
. local (municipal), regional and "departemental" organisations
. institutions and companies dependent upon the state, e.g., SNCF (National Railways) EDF (Power & Light), RATP (public transport), hospitals

We will take a look at the progress of an operation by examining its successive phases.

### Programme
2.    The Owner is required to prepare or have prepared a building programme in which the following information is provided:

. **Data**
    This primarily concerns site-relevant information: (topographic surveys, preliminary soil surveys, geographic, seismic and climatic data, drawings of existing roadways and networks)

. **Requirements**
    This includes in particular the floor area, spatial and inter-connecting requirements needed to cover the functional aspects of the building(s) as well as the standard of quality to be attained for the works and technical installations

. **Constraints**
Of which the Owner is aware -- Compliance with regulations of a technical, urbanistic or other order

. **Conditions**
These comprise the conditions imposed by the Owner on the Designer/Engineer (or Architectural & Engineering Team). They can either be of a technical or financial order:
. imperative date for completion
. maximum cost
. standard of quality

The programme file is prepared by a specialist consultant and a competition may or may not be held.

## Public Designer/Engineer or A & E Team
3. Some Public Authorities possess large technical departments and carry out the A & E assignment themselves; this is the case for civil engineering works such as bridges, roadways, airports and nuclear power plants, for example. I will not go into this case in detail since the contract(s) for the works is (are) identical to contracts with private Designer/Engineers.

4. Before continuing, we must first define the concept of "A & E team":

*" A person or corporate body grouping together the* Architectural, Technical *and* Financial *functions and who is requested by the Owner to design the project, to supervise execution of the works and monitor their compliance, and to propose commissioning and payment."*

## Private A & E Team
5. In this case, the Public Sector Owner entrusts the A & E assignment to participants in the private sector. Three basic principles govern an A & E assignment for a public project:
. the unicity of the A & E team,
. the setting up a design competition among A & E teams,
. awarding the project on the basis of the targeted cost

## Unicity of the A & E team
6. The Owner signs one contract only with the A & E team, which is usually composed of:
. an Architect/Designer
. an Engineering design office or Consulting Engineers
. specialist engineers (acoustics, safety) if required, and possibly an estimator

7.    The A & E team is legally represented to the Owner by an Agent/Delegate, but the team's responsibility is a <u>joint</u> responsibility.    Relationships  among  team  members  are co-contracting relationships.

8.    It should be pointed out that in France, the Building Permit must be signed by an Architect who can only be either free lance or salaried by an architectural firm (Law of January 3rd, 1977 petaining to Architecture).  The legal tie between the Owner and the Architect must be direct.

## Design Competition
9.    The Owner organises a competition among A & E design teams  on  the  basis  of  his  programme.   For  prestigious projects,  the  design  competition  can  be  nationwide  or international;  in this case, there are two rounds:
. the first round is based on a general design concept
  accompanied by a few sketches,
. the 3 or 4 candidates selected from the first round must
  then prepare a partial Preliminary or Schematic Design.

10.   Generally speaking, losing teams are provided with remuneration which covers only part of their expenses.

## Targeted Cost
11.   During the design competition the Designers submit the following along with conceptual design studies:

. an estimate of the cost of works, called the "Targeted
  Cost" (cost of works + the A & E team fees)
. a lump sum fee

12.   Public contracts include penality clauses when the targeted cost is not respected (a certain margin is allowed, however).

13.   A schedule of rates also exists for A & E team fees, but it is only given as an indication.  The distribution of fees within the A & E design team is mutually agreed upon by the partners.  Their accord is drawn up in the form of a agreement defining both the distribution of fees and tasks. The Owner is usually informed as to the contents of this agreement.

## Types of Assignments
14.   For the design study phase, one of two types of assignments is normally used:

. An M2 assignment which includes:
  . the Preliminary or Schematic Design,
  . Design Development
  . the bid documents, bid analysis, and contract
    preparation & award assistance

In this case, the working drawings are executed by the Contractor.

. An M1 type assignment which, in addition to the tasks included in an M2 assignment, also includes the Working Drawings.

15.  In both cases, the A & E team is responsible for the following during the execution of the works:

. supervising the construction works and monitoring their compliance
. the financial management of the siteworks,
. the detailed commissioning of the completed project
. the as-built drawings

Within the framework of its assignment, the A & E team supervises all additional works and investigates any requests or claims made by contractor(s).

16.  Additional assignments concerning maintenance organisation and management are currently being incorporated into A & E team tasks as early on as the conceptual phase, given the importance these considerations now have in regards to the viability of the works.

### Building Control Authority

17.  For most construction operations, the law stipulates that the project must be monitored by a Building Control Authority.  This specialised organisation must be completely independent from A & E teams and Contractors and their work is limited exclusively to carrying out monitoring assignments.

18.  Their assignment covers the solidity of the work and the safety of persons in terms of the law.  A Building Control Authority monitoring assignment includes:
. examining the architectural and structural drawings as well as the documents concerning the foundations
. ascertaining the compliance of the works with regards to Regulations
. carrying out site visits to ensure correct installation. This task, however, is intermittent and only concerns certain works;  it therefore does not cover a second time the A & E team's monitoring assignment, which is continuous and for all works.

### Construction Works Contracts

Contract Type
19.  Contracts for construction works are generally lump sum fee contracts, except possibly for a few works connected with the ground (foundations).  The contract sets up the

assumptions for the lump sum fee and the Contractor is paid
either more or less in relation to these assumptions (length
of piles, for example). Within the framework of an M1
assignment, the A & E team prepares a bill of quantities for
the Owner which is not transmitted to bidding contractors.
Each contractor has to define quantities in his bid as they
do not constitute part of the contract. Unitary prices are
used to readjust estimates in relation to the lump sum fee.

**Organisation of Contracting**
20.    There are normally three possibilities:

20.a) <u>Contract by trade</u>
    In this case, the Owner signs from 20 to 30 contracts
    with the various contracting firms. The advantage of
    this type of procedure is that it allows the Owner to
    call for bids from many firms and to become acquainted
    with many contractors; it also leaves more room for
    negotiations. He generally obtains better prices, but:

    . the administrative management of the site is much more
      complex
    . he has no guarantee against the default of a given
      contractor
    . he must entrust the A & E team or a specialist
      consultant with an assignment encompassing scheduling,
      project coordination and site management.

    With this type of set up, the siteworks can be started
    up very early on and time saved in terms of the overall
    time for completion. Indeed, it is not necessary to
    have completed the design documents for all trades in
    order to call for bids and designate contractors for
    earthworks, foundation works and structural works, for
    example.

    In this case, the A & E team's task is more complex
    because it must clearly define in detail the limits of
    works among the building trades to avoid any omissions
    or repetitions.

20.b) <u>General Contracting Contract</u>
    In this case, the Owner signs one contract only and
    deals with a single general contracting firm responsible
    for executing all the construction works. Management is
    of course simpler and the Owner is protected against the
    default of any of the General Contractor's subcontrac-
    tors.

    The cost is generally higher in this case than with
    separate contracts by trade, and the design file must be
    entirely completed before bids can be requested from
    Contractors.

20.c) <u>Grouped Contractors Contract</u>
This type of contract resembles a general contracting contract since the Group's <u>Agent/Delegate</u> is responsible for the default of any of its co-contractors. The principal difference is that all the participating co-contractors and the cost of their respective trades is known. This kind of "transparency" doesn't exist in agreements signed with a general contractor.

21. Owners in the public sector use the General Contracting procedure for small and average-size projects especially, whereas the trade-by-trade contract set up is usually employed for large projects. For example, the following very large construction operations in Paris:
. The Ministry of Finance building
. The Bastille Opera House
. The Grand Arch at La Défense
. The Louvre Museum
were all built using trade-by-trade contracts.

## New Assignment Schemes

22. The schemes described above for architectural and engineering assignments and construction works contracts constitute the majority of cases; there are, however, some interesting new arrangements, such as:

## Design and Build

23. On the basis of a building programme and technical specifications precisely defining the technical performances which the works must provide (i.e., level of soundproofing, fire integrity rating, etc.) the Owner organises a call for bids from teams composed of a General Contractor, an Architect and a Engineering Design Office. Bid submittals include both the design studies and a contract for the construction works. The design concept and construction works assignments are thus concentrated in a single and same contract.

24. This procedure is used in building sectors where the work is urgent and where there is a possibility of a series of projects (teaching establishments, programme for prisons, etc.). In this case, the Designer/Engineer's position is difficult because he must defend the interests of the Owner with regard to the General Contractor, with whom he is also associated.

## Overall Cost

25. A & E teams are increasingly aware of the operating and maintenance costs for the completed project. Calls for bids from contracting firms now sometimes require the tenderer to submit a bid not only for the construction

works, but also for the maintenance and repair of the building and its installations for a 10-year period. The bid submitted is analysed in terms of the cost overall. This practice concerns in part scholastic buildings, hospitals and public office buildings.


## OPERATIONS IN THE PRIVATE SECTOR

26.    This concerns construction operations which are not regulated by public sector contracts (see paragraph 1). As there are no specific obligations for private projects, I will outline the procedures used the most frequently.

### A & E Team
27.    The Owner generally signs separate contracts with the Architect, the Engineering Office and the Consulting Engineers. For large operations (bank headquarters, oil companies), the Owner organises a Design Competition. Sometimes the Architect is chosen directly because of his renown.

28.    A design competition is the general rule and lump sum fees are negotiated after launching the competition.

29.    Sometimes the Engineering Office or the Consulting Engineers are the Architect's sub-contractors as well.

30.    The types of assignments entrusted to the A & E team are very similar to those described for an operation in the public sector.

### Building Control Authority
31.    The Building Control Authority has the same responsibilities and carries out the same assignment for private projects that it ensures for public constructions.

### Construction Works Contracts
32.    The same set up as for public contracts is used for most operations: either a general contracting contract or trade-by-trade contracts.

33.    There is a French Standard (NF P 03 001) defining general arrangements for contracts; compliance with this regulation is not obligatory, but it is customarily referred to in contract preparation.

34. Sometimes turnkey contracts are organised; in addition to project design and construction, these contracts include other services such as site acquisition, financing, operation and maintenance. These contracts are proposed by companies which are subsidiaries of large construction corporations.

35. Construction Management is employed very little in France, probably because French A & E teams are very attached to the idea of lump sum remuneration.

# 5. Project organisation and implementation in the German civil engineering industry

J. J. P. HAENSEL, FIE Aust, VDI, Ingenieurbuero HRA,
Haensel-Roik-Albrecht & Partners

SYNOPSIS. This paper describes the project organization and implementation in the civil industry in Germany. A short summary
of the legal basis is given. The individual roles of the owner,the designer, public and civil supervisor and the contractor
during planning and construction are presented. Financial control and handling of variations and claims is briefly mentioned.

THE LEGAL BASIS FOR PLANNING, CONSTRUCTION AND IMPLEMENTATION

The German legal system consists of written law and distin-
guishes between public law, with the state as the sovereign and
civil law laying down the rules of composition between bodies
of natural or legal origin.

Building and construction effects the public sector as well as
the individual. To understand the procedures of project organization and implementation in Germany a short introduction concerning the legal basis is essential.

1.    Public law

Any building and construction procedures are subject of the
federal legislation as well as that of the states. There is no
clear distinction in the federal constitution about their individual responsibilities. In special cases this has been dealt
with by federal court judgement, for example for roads, railways and waterways and energy supply.

Planning can be subdivided into global and regional master
planning.

1.1    Global master planning
       (Raumordnung)

Scope of the global master planning is the determination and
coordination of the utilisation of land between the federal republic, the states and individual regions. There exists federal
and coordinated state legislation, which is binding for

the planning administrations. Public participation is not possible.

## 1.2 Regional master planning
(Bauleitplanung)

The actual regional planning is left to the local community and this is the key to the understanding of the structure of the German construction industry, consisting of a great number of small, local companies and a close network of local representation of the big companies.

The regional master planning consists of two consecutive steps:

### 1.2.1 Regional utilisation planning
(Flächennutzungsplan)

In a first step the local community designates the way of utilisation of land, for example for housing, recreation, industrial use or other purposes. This is a prerogative of the community with no possibility of public or private intervention.

### 1.2.2 Local building and construction planning
(Bebauungsplan)

Details for futher planning are given in the next step. These details cover for example the maximum permissible height of buildings, the allowable floor area relative to the land area, location of streets, the types of possible industrial use, etc.

This planning stage is publicly announced, layed open and is open to public and private intervention. This is the most time-consuming planning stage due to the duration of legal proceedings. The final planning concept becomes legal character by formal resolution of the community.

In the case of public building and construction activities for example roads, railways, waterways, airports, etc. a similar, but stricter procedure is required, the so-called "Planfeststellungsverfahren".

## 1.3 General building and construction legislation
(Bauordnungsrecht)

The detailed building and construction legislation is responsibility of the states (Landesbauordnung). It is referred to as "public building code" in the following. Each state has its own public building code which differs in each case slightly from a federal model code, the so-called "Musterbauordnung".

The public building code settles minimum requirements regarding the layout of buildings, fire protection requirements, building supply and it prescribes the procedures of public approval and public control of building projects and implementation.

### 1.3.1 Public building control instances
(Bauaufsicht)

There are communal, regional and state building authorities. A superior authority is the "Institut für Bautechnik" in Berlin which is mainly involved in the certification of building materials and structural members.

### 1.3.2 Public building permit
(Baugenehmigung)

The communal public building authority (Bauordnungsamt) gives the clearance to proceed with construction when the design is in accordance with the state building code, the structural design is in accordance with the relevant DIN - codes or other technical building codes and the materials to be used are certified.

The building authority may commission the check of the structural analysis, the design drawings and the workshop drawings, the structural fire protection, heat consumption and sound absorption to an officially appointed "Prüfingenieur" (Proof-Engineer).

### 1.3.3 Public construction supervision
(Bauüberwachung)

The construction is supervised by the communal building authority or by the proof-engineer. This supervision is not continuous (spot checks). The responsibility remains with the contractor.

### 1.4 Autonomous public authorities

In addition to the building authorities there are other autonomous authorities for roads, waterways, railways and some specialized military purposes. Their structure is similar to that of the building authorities.

### 2. Civil law

German civil legislation is laid down in the BGB - "Bürgerliches Gesetzbuch". The BGB is the legal basis of the contractural terms between owner, designer and contractor. Not only the German BGB but also all other legal systems do not contain regulations especially designed for building and construction procedures. To meet this demand of clear contractural terms, the VOB - "Verdingungsordnung für Bauleistungen" (Contractural term for building and construction works) has been introduced in Germany. The VOB has no legal status. The contracting parties must make it part of their agreement.

In the international field the "Conditions of Contract (International) for Work of Civil Engineering Construction"

have been developped, named after the "Federation Internationale des Ingeniers-Conseils" the FIDIC contractural terms.
The FIDIC differs from the VOB significantly. It is much more
detailed and gives the engineer a central position in the
building process. The VOB does not even mention the consulting
engineer or the architect. This is dealt with in the state
building regulations (see 1.3). The FIDIC is partly contra-
dictory to the usual conduct of building and construction work
in Germany and is virtually unknown internally.

### 2.1    BGB - contracts

The BGB is the superior law. Thus, it is always basis of
contracts and claims. Architekts, engineers and other consultants work on the basis of BGB-contracts. Building and construction contracts based on the BGB alone are unusual, the VOB and
special additional contractural terms would complete the agreement between the parties involved.

### 2.2    The VOB

The German contractural terms for building and construction
works consist of three parts VOB/A, /B and/C.

The VOB/A deals with the "General rules concerning the allocation (placing of contracts) of civil engineering works", by
public corporations.

The most important part, the VOB/B, contains the "General
contractural terms for the implementation of civil engineering
works". It deals with the relationship between owner and
contractor, their rights and obligations **after** placing of the
contract. Among other subjects it covers payments, flow of
documents, conduct of construction, construction schedules,
impediments and interruption of works, allocation of risks,
notice of agreement, penalties, acceptance procedures, warranty
and claims.

The VOB/C contains the "General technical rules for civil engineering works" and is of less importance in this context.

PROJECT ORGANIZATION AND IMPLEMENTATION

A simplified flow chart of a building process is given on the
following page.

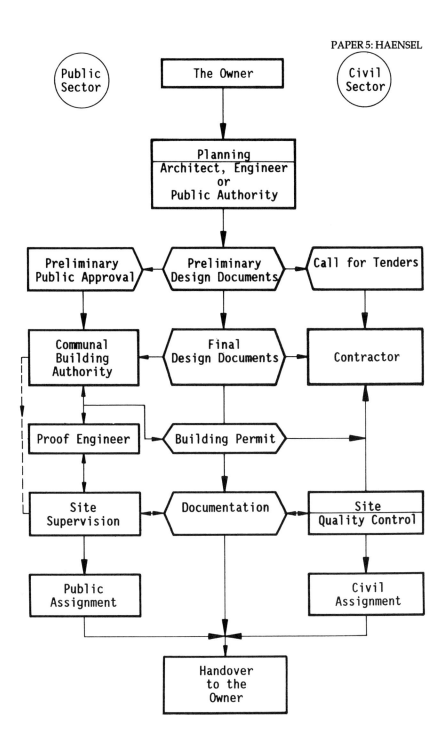

Basis Flow Chart of a Building Process

This flow chart is subdivided into different stages and participants in the vertical direction and the public and civil sector across the sheet.

### 1.    Planning stage

As a first step the owner commissions the qualified planning of
his intentions to an architect or engineer. In the case of
public authorities owner and planner are often identical. They
prepare the preliminary design and the tender documents. These
documents must go into details and must be definite in describing the intentions of the designer (see VOB). The bill of
quantities should be accurate within 10% to avoid subsequent
variations to the contract. Parallel to the call for tender the
preliminary design documents are submitted to the communal
building authority for the first step of public approval, to
check whether the design is in accordance with the state building regulations.

In the case of public building and construction activities the
above mentioned "Planfeststellungsverfahren" covers this first
step of public approval.

### 2.    Types of contracts

The different types of contracts are commonly known: standard
and flat rate contracts, hourly rates and cost plus contracts.
The standard rate contract is the most common form for the
implementation of the tender design.

Many calls for tender in Germany for large projects will ask
for alternative design proposals, especially in the public
building and construction sector. If such an alternative proposal is chosen for implementation the flat rate contract is a
logical consequence.

The other types of contracts are insignificant in this context.

### 3.    Contracting

In most cases of small and medium sized building projects, the
planner - usually an architect - lets the contracts on behalf
of the owner to the various trades and crafts on the basis of
his tender documents. The contracts are let to each individual
contractor on a "design and construct"- basis and they become
responsible for the correct execution of their work in accordance with VOB/C, the DIN-codes and other technical, administrative rulings. The "architect" will take over the coordination
of the project. He controls the building progress on the basis
of VOB/B and the special conditions of his tender documents. He
controls the financial proceedings, the flow of documents, certification, the assignment procedures and arranges the final
handover to the owner. He has to handle variations and claims
and finally present them to the owner for payment. Parties in

legal proceeding are the owner and the contractor. The owner may sue the "architect" for faults or negligence.

The role of the architects in Germany in the building industry is a very strong one. They are represented locally, or are often local consultants with close contacts to real estate and political sources.

For large sized building, turn-key contracts, a commonly known contractual basis, are chosen. The owner/designer lets the contract on fixed contractural and financial terms. The internal structure of "the contractor" and the contractural interdependency between the various subcontractors would be similar to that laid out above. In most cases special consultants are engaged additionally for the coordination of the project, site organisation and control of progress and the flow of finance.

For other large size building and construction projects, especially in the public sector, several construction companies would share the job under the designation "Arbeitsgemeinschaft", or short "ARGE" on the basis of a "design and construct"- contract. One of these companies takes over the external professional and legal responsibilities. The public authority acts as the owner /planner (architect). The internal contractural structure between the construction companies involved is similar to that described in the first paragraph.

For some large international investments in the civil sector, major German construction companies have taken over the risk and responsibility for ownership, planning, design and construction until completion of the whole project. The ownership is rearranged after completion.

4. The flow of design documents

The general design documents, the basic design drawings and the structural analysis has to be handed over to the local building authority. The authority will check these documents or commission this to a proof engineer, as mentioned above.

With the approval, these documents become public documents. One publicly approved copy is handed out to each of the parties involved. The presentation and format of these documents is subject to certain legal requirements and generally accepted rulings. They must not only be readable, the general assumptions, the analysis itself and the results must be presented clearly to allow an independent verification and duplification of the design analysis and their results.

Upon public approval of these design documents the building permit is awarded. The approval of the detailed design drawings or workshop drawings should be finished prior to the start of construction but this is usually a process parallel to the construction work.

The proof engineer works on behalf of the local public building authority. There is no legal relationship to the owner, the designer or the contractor. He is paid by the authority, costs which are reimbursed by the owner. In public civil activities, the position of planner and owner are usually combined. In these cases independent proof engineers are mandatory.

The authority or the proof engineer will make spot checks during construction to ensure that the basic public requirements of project implementation and documentation of quality control are adhered to. Parts of the quality control documents, e.g. concrete grade certificates and welding certificates are included in the public documentation.

### 5.    The building site

On site the "responsible site manager" (verantwortlicher Bauleiter) is the person with the ultimate managerial, legal, contractural and financial responsibility for the work on site. This wide definition of work affiliation to one person is unsatisfactory and generally criticized.

The handling of variations, claims and accounting is laid down in the VOB/B. It is scope of the work of the above mentioned site manager, who would supervise but delegate this work.

The guaranty and liability period in the building contract is mostly agreed upon to be five years, in accordance with the BGB. The basic period in accordance with the VOB would be only two years. In cases of negligence the liability period may be extended by a civil court to thirty years, so far a hypothetical possibility.

### 6.    Acceptance of works

The site manager has to control and document the work on site, to achieve intermediate acceptance of works, as the basis for the accounting procedures and to reach final civil assignment. The procedures are laid down in the VOB/B and partly VOB/C.

The public assignment by the authority or the proof engineer - the statement that the building or structure has been erected in accordance with the approved design documents and that it is regarded safe for subsequent use - allows further civil legal and contractural proceedings for the contractor and planner towards the final handover to the owner.

References:

**Clemm, N.**: Bauvertragsrecht
Technische Universität Berlin
Universitätsbibliothek, Abt. Publikationen
Straße des 17. Juni 135, D-1000 Berlin 12

**Ingenstau, Korbion**: VOB, Teil A und B, Kommentar
Werner Verlag, Düsseldorf

**Mittag, M.**: VOB/C-Praxis-Kommentar
Weka Fachverlage GmbH
Römerstr. 4, D-8901 Kissing

# 6. Construction management in the UK

J. A. ARMITT, FICE, FBIM, Joint Managing Director, John Laing
Construction Ltd

INTRODUCTION. Other papers in this conference address the
issue of overall project management. The management of the
construction phase is one in which many parties will have a
hand but which for its success relies largely on the
capability of the Contractors.

1. Today we see an increasing incidence of the
Contractors also being responsible for design and, on
occasion, the raising of finance.
2. The first of these trends provides an opportunity to
remedy many of the problems that plague the whole
construction process. Closer integration of design and
construct processes will bring our industry closer to that
of the car and aeroplane industries where manufacturing
processes are related to design development to ensure
minimum manufacturing cost and maximum efficiency.
However, 95% of Civil Engineering and 80% of Building
construction in UK still separates design responsibility,
leaving the Contractors to do the best they can with a
design which is handed down with little or no discussion on
its buildability. This paper, therefore, will concentrate
on examining how the Contractors manage their
responsibility to convert a design into the finished
product.
3. A contractor's role is to manage the prime resources
of labour, plant and materials in order to produce a
product which meets its specification within a planned
period and a pre-forecast cost.
4. The last of these is the key to the continuation in
business of the contractor who in the UK must make a profit
to pay a dividend to his shareholders. The start of the
process, the pricing of the project probably in a
competitive tender situation, is vital.

THE TENDER
5. Success in the tender process is firstly seen as
winning the project almost certainly with the lowest price.
Accepting that a contractor wishes to have the maximum
amount of money possible with which to work, this lowest
price is ideally lowest by a very small margin, 1% or less.

With net profit for construction operations typically at 2-4% of turnover, every percentage point gap between the low bidder and the next highest is a cause of rueful frustration.

6. In a large construction company, every day of the year requires the winning of about £4m worth of work on average represented on average by four separate contracts.

7. Cynics will say that the more detail and more attention a contractor gives to the tender process, the more likely his price is to be higher. In other words, many jobs are won by default. As with all cynicism, there will be more than a grain of truth in the observation. It is therefore important that a contractor does not overload his estimating office if he wishes to achieve his workload by design rather than accident.

8. Attention to detail reaps its own rewards and so it is with the tender process. The more options the contractor is able to study with regard to his temporary works, the more programme alternatives, the more traffic management options, the more materials suppliers and subcontractors are considered, the more chance there is of arriving at the cheapest but effective solution. Detailed attention to three bids at the same time rather than the same resource over five bids will lead to success for the right reasons. This needs to be recognised not only by contractors but by clients and their engineers or architects.

9. An important element of the tender process is the assessment of risk. Risk is directly related to the conditions of contract. The cost reimbursable contract carries no risk to the contractor but a lot to the client. At the other extreme is the fixed price lump sum with no remeasurement of quantities. Both are rare but in recent years the UK industry has seen a trend particularly by private sector clients in the building sector to adapt standard forms of contract so as to place more onus and risk on the contractor. Most contractors will rise to the challenge but clients should recognise that tender prices and contractual conflict will likely rise as well.

10. Forcing contractors to price the unknown in a competitive market reduces the probability of the tender sum accurately reflecting the cost of the work. What is the scope? is a regular question in any tender assessment. It means on the one hand what is the probability of obtaining lower prices for materials and subcontractors than those given at the time of tender and on the other what is the probability of the engineer and client changing the type and quantity of the works leading to variations and claims.

11. Both are legitimate questions. The project at tender stage which has limited information produced over a short period will give the contractor most cause for expectation of variation and claim. It is no good complaining that contractors bid low and seek their profit through claims.

It is an inevitable result of market forces in which
insufficient preparation by the client and his advisors will
lead to delay, disruption and expense.  Poor information is
more of a risk for the client than for the contractor.
Contract forms which impose tight programme periods, apply
heavy liquidated damages, resist the variation of rates,
ignore the impact of external events on a contractor's
activities, have increased in the UK in recent years.  They
increase the contractor's risk, they reduce the accuracy of
his tender, are more likely to give rise to claims and do
nothing to promote a sense of team spirit so necessary for a
successful project.

12. Having been awarded a contract, the contractor is now
faced with the task for which his expertise has been honed -
the efficient management of resources.  These resources are
his own management and technical staff, his own labour, his
own plant and increasingly the staff labour and plant of
subcontractors and, of course, materials.  Materials also
may either be supplied by the main contractor or the
subcontractors or, occasionally, direct by the client.

MANAGERIAL AND TECHNICAL STAFF

13. People are the key asset of any contractor.  In the UK
the managerial and technical staff will be long term
employees.

14. There is a continuing trend towards specialisation.
Engineering, Planning, Procurement, Quantity Surveying,
Accountants, Inspection, labour management, project
management, are all separate tasks and all are carried out
by people who have been trained, obtained qualifications,
and specialise in one of the tasks.  They represent 4 - 8%
of a contract's direct cost.

15. Educational qualifications continue to rise but all
will have joined a contractor by the age of 22.  People with
doctorates are rare recruits to a contractor.

16. Graduates whether they are Engineers, Quantity
Surveyors or Management Trainees will all be required to
start doing what are often considered mundane tasks but
which provide an insight and understanding of the full
construction process.  Mobility of staff, once a hallmark
of construction, is today less likely.  This, in addition
to the local market attitude of clients and contractors
leads to strong regionalisation of businesses.  The trend
is stronger in Building than Civil Engineering but is an
increasing problem in the latter.  The causes are the
demand for more leisure time, a more stable home, working
wives with their own professions and a generally buoyant
market.

17. Site staff will usually work around a 50-hour week but
often more, particularly in Civil Engineering.  Overtime
beyond 40 hours will be paid to junior staff but less likely
to those in positions of responsibility or authority.

18. The smaller the project, the greater the pressure to minimise the number of staff and seek role flexibility. These are creditable aims in respect of cost reduction but the key to successful construction is the right materials in the right place at the right time. Most contractors in recent years have recognised the pursuit of excellence or 'get it right first time'. This is more likely to be achieved if the site team is not overstretched but able to provide full technical skill to the task.

19. When projects are going wrong, it usually results in the sending in of additional staff, and the conclusion is obvious.

20. Contractors carry out nearly all the training of their staff in-house. Site managers are notorious for not wishing to release people for off-site training. There is still a tendency for on the job learning to be considered all that is necessary, but the expectation of young people and the realisation by employers that cutting the training budget every time there is a market fall only causes more problems in the longer term, is leading to an increase in formal training, particularly beyond that required to achieve a technical or professional qualification. One area traditionally neglected and where learning on the job was considered sufficient was that of first/second line supervision or the Foreman. These men are in fact the backbone of the industry but it is only recently that their need for formal off-site training on a regular basis has been recognised. Most recently steps have been taken to provide recognised qualifications.

21. Successful management of a site team is the result of good and effective communication. Daily review meetings, the clear setting of achievable goals, examination of the causes of failure, constant review of short term programmes, are all vital ingredients.

22. Project management is team management, and the analogy to a sporting team in which individual skills are combined and mutual support provided, with a captain who is seeing all elements of the task, is clear.

23. Professional qualifications over and beyond academic qualifications are a common feature of UK construction professionals. The achievement of a degree will be followed by further exams and tests of experience in order to become members of professional associations which are essential for peer recognition. Attainment of these qualifications will occur between the age of 24-28 depending on the discipline.

LABOUR

24. Until the late 1970's, the majority of construction labour was employed under the terms of National Agreements by the main contractors.

25. Through the 1980's, this has steadily changed to the point where today 50% of the construction labour force is self-employed. The self-employed either work on an

individual basis or provide their services to a labour
subcontractor who will co-ordinate and manage their
activities for a main contractor.

26. The basic wage rate provided by the National Agreements
is low and for a standard 39 hour week would provide about
50-60% of the National average wage.

27. Wages are therefore brought up to what is a market
level by second tier bonus payments. Typically the hours
worked are also increased by an average of a further 8
hours. The combination of the two, together with travel
allowances, can double the basic wage.

28. Labour only subcontractors will often not use the
National Agreement but pay a flat rate for a 9-hour shift.
The second tier payments also enable regional variations to
come into effect. Thus in London the second tier might be
100% of base rate and in Cornwall or Cumbria, only 30%.

29. The extent to which wages are a reflection of
productivity varies. Many tasks on a construction site,
e.g. crane drivers, forklift operators, cannot be targetted.
Others, e.g. bricklayers or steelfixers, can be easily
measured. On the largest projects detailed bonus schemes
are operated by the major contractors using their own direct
labour. On smaller sites a more approximate form of
targetting is used based on an understanding between labour
and management as to what needs to be produced in a week in
order to maintain programme. The smaller subcontractor will
know clearly in his mind the outputs he needs from his men
in order to make a profit and will quickly dismiss those who
are not up to the mark.

30. The growth in self-employment and subcontracted labour
has not surprisingly, resulted in a significant decline in
Trade Union membership. Today, less than one third of the
labour force are Union members.

31. Demographic forecasts, combined with social trends,
mean that the construction industry will have an
increasingly difficult task attracting young people. This
is recognised by most large employers and the Trade Unions.
It is resulting in pressure to increase basic wages and
improve training.

32. Training is largely carried out on the job and the old
formal apprenticeship schemes are in decline. They have
been replaced by shorter term schemes but the increase in
self-employment and subcontracting has resulted in less
craft training. With the mobile and disparate nature of the
industry, this is a difficult problem to resolve. What is
clear is that the responsibility lies with employers. The
increased mobility of labour within Europe can, of course,
help individual countries to cope with peaks in demand.
This movement of labour has already started and can only be
expected to increase.

33. An area of concern is the extent to which EEC
legislation will seek to remove national variations in terms
and conditions of employment. Competition within

Europe is a vital ingredient to the region's development
and any steps to legislate European levels of pay, whether
to labour or engineers, should be resisted.  The Social
Charter has already shown a lack of understanding of the
nature of the construction industry with its desire to
control overtime and shift working practices.  Appropriate
representation is being made by UK and other European
employers.

MATERIALS
34. The efficient specification, procurement and delivery
on time is central to project success.
35. In the UK the specification of which materials are to
be used is laid down by the Consulting Engineer and
Architect.  In a design and construct contract the
contractor will have more say in the decision but the lead
will still be taken by the consultants.
36. For the contractor, the extent to which materials are
nominated in terms of specific suppliers will have a direct
influence on his ability to save money on his tender
allowances.  The greater the degree of nomination, the less
opportunity to shop around for alternatives.  The judgments
made at tender stage by a contractor on his ability to
obtain reductions on the prices quoted are key judgments.
Materials can represent 60% of a contract cost, and the
ability to know current market rates and how they will move
during the contract period is vital.  Procurement on the
large projects £10m plus will probably be carried out by
purchasing staff based on site.  The smaller projects will
be procured from a Head of Regional office.
37. In either case, it will be done by specialist staff
skilled in the task of knowing the market, prices, and with
an ability to negotiate terms and conditions of contract.
38. For a civil engineering project, local knowledge is
vital and information of local geology and potential borrow
pits can be the key to a lower tender.  Placing an order
for 5000 $m^3$ of stone or 50 door sets is not the end of the
procurement process.  Monitoring delivery and quality and
then ensuring proper storage on site are equally important.
The end objective is to have the right quantity of the
correct quality in the hands of the craftsmen at the right
time.
39. The site team are faced with a series of conflicting
but inter-related issues.  In a falling market, put off the
order as long as possible to get the best price, press for
delivery but do not have too much material on site before it
is needed.  The latter is difficult to avoid if, in a rising
market, you have ordered early.  Manufacturers have
mechanised their packing, loading and offloading
procedures.  On sites, very little development has taken
place apart from the now ubiquitous forklift truck and most
material deliveries have to be broken down and distributed
to diffent locations with the attendant risk of loss and
damage.
56

40. Fast track construction on commercial buildings has, through contractor input, resulted in prefabrication of toilet and lift units whilst cladding units have become more and more high quality prefabrications on occasion containing steel frame, brick or stone cladding and glazing, all pre-assembled. These are welcome moves but only economically possible on the large developments.

41. Architects' desire to make every building different from exterior to door handle means that the vast majority of projects are procured and erected piecemeal. Again development of the European market will serve to widen the options so that contractor's buyers will need to widen their knowledge base of what can be bought where and at what price. Entry by Britain into the Exchange Rate Mechanism will at least reduce a further risk arising from exchange rates. The increased complexity of the whole procurement process has and will continue to encourage the use of computers for data storage and retrieval and the electronic transfer of orders and invoices.

42. On sites, contractor's stores are also increasingly computer controlled areas although like the card index systems they have replaced, they are of little use unless constantly updated by the stores staff.

43. To summarise, the future will mean a wider source of materials, a need for more staff with language abilities, greater use of the computer and a continuing but not rapid development of mechanised material placement methods.

PLANT

44. Twenty years ago most contractors owned all or most of their constructing plant. Today only the largest companies have a large plant holding. That holding will be smaller than it used to be and will be available for hire to other contractors just as much as it is available for internal use.

45. Most plant today is owned by a multitude of plant hire companies. The reasons for the change are the shift to subcontracting and the rigorous control of assets in contractor's organisations. On a building project all the plant except maybe the tower crane will be hired by a contractor.

46. On a large Civil Engineering project more of the very heavy plant will be owned by the contractor but here again rigorous comparisons will have been made between the cost of the asset and the external hire rate.

47. The result of all the above is a highly competitive plant hire market which, like the contractors, is made up of a few major players and a whole host of much smaller companies appearing and disappearing on a regular basis. Like the labour force, the amount of plant on site is constantly monitored for effective and efficient usage. Records of working hours are maintained so that it can be off-hired as soon as usage drops below an effective level.

In the UK, plant hirers operate a certification system of driver competence although this is not a mandatory requirement other than that required under the general requirements of Health and Safety legislation.

48. Looking to the future, it seems unlikely there will be any major changes in the way construction plant is provided. With regard to robotics, there is little activity in this field. The level of investment required is high and, apart from one DTI sponsored initiative for wall climbing inspection, the lack of quick returns on investment gives little encouragement for UK initiatives.

SUBCONTRACTORS

49. As has been mentioned several times in this paper, there has been steady growth in specialised contractors in the last 20 years. So much so that on many projects the construction management process is centred solely on the management and organisation of subcontractors.

50. Arguably, the growth of companies who specialise in a particular element of construction and the resultant competition should improve techniques and productivity. This is probably true for straightforward projects but on complex work the incentive for the subcontractor is less and he will have to rely on his minority of highly skilled employees.

51. For the large contractors, the use of subcontractors is a two-edged sword. On the one hand it enables them to reduce overheads, provides more flexibility and improves cash flow and asset usage. On the other, it reduces their direct control over events and when these go awry, their reputation is at risk. In addition, it reduces their own skill base particularly in the area of first line supervision.

52. Main contractors are now realising that it is essential to work very closely with their subcontractors helping them achieve maximum productivity and even helping them to train and develop staff. Discussion and debate continues as to whether the UK will see continuation of the subcontracting solution or a return to direct labour. At present there is no reason to expect the latter, but to assume that subject to market conditions subcontractors as in America will develop and enhance their own performance. For main contractors, particularly in the building sector, the task is therefore that of co-ordination, support, provision of interface services, continuous monitoring of progress and quality.

QUALITY

53. For many years the management of quality within the site construction process was a case of visual inspection, concrete cubes, possibly some off site testing of fire resistance and air or water tests on piped services. Suppliers would occasionally provide test certificates of

their materials which were filed and forgotten.

54. In the last ten years, the requirements of the oil and nuclear sectors, together with a more litigious environment and also recognition by contractors that rework is expensive, have combined to produce a more quality conscious ethic. Clients, engineers, contractors have all learnt about Quality Assurance and how it can benefit the project. That a contractor should be certified to BS5750 is still only rarely mandated. This has not stopped contractors from realising that to operate their business in a Quality Assurance regime can be beneficial. It does add to costs in the form of QA engineers, extra inspectors, more paperwork, but it also saves money by reducing abortive work, by giving the buyer more information about the materials he is expediting and by reducing the potential of claims arising from faulty workmanship or materials.

55. Many companies now contain the word 'excellence' in their publicity. All have realised that saying you strive for excellence is providing a stick with which to be beaten unless you actively instal and audit the procedures necessary to achieve excellence.

56. It is an area in which we expect to see continued development and improvement.

PROJECT CONTROLS

57. On site activities are managed and organised by a team of people who are brought together for that particular project. Some will have worked together before but not all. A contractor therefore needs a recognised and established control framework within which the team can very quickly commence work.

58. The estimators and tender team will have made a whole series of judgements and amusements in arriving at the tender sum. Setting aside variations and claims profit for the contractor is achieved by working within that tender sum.

59. The first thing the Site team need therefore is that tender sum in detail in other words a budget. This must be produced by the estimators quickly in a form easily understood. It will break down the labour plant materials staff subcontract elements of each part of the work. Computers today enable this to be done quickly ideally coding elements so that budget, orders, invoices, cost codes and valuations can all be quickly interrelated.

60. The majority of the site team will not have been involved in the tender. They will therefore have their own ideas of how tasks can be carried out. As they will be the people identified at the end of the day as responsible for the sucess of the project their ideas will take precedence.

61. It is very important however that an early transfer of ideas and assumptions from the estimating team to the site team takes place. With the work underway what are the control procedures used by a contractor?

62. Daily. Labour clocks in and out; if a bonus scheme is in operation working hours are allocated to tasks. Targets are established for new tasks. Site supervision are working to a programme of activities received and updated each morning or evening. The quantity surveyors will be measuring the volume of work completed.

63. Materials delivered will be recorded, materials used will be recorded, wasteage recorded. Plant hours worked will be recorded. Records of all instructions received from the Engineer and of all variations noted will be kept and passed to the Quantity Surveyors.

64. Weekly. Labour, plant and staff costs will be recorded and presented on a report which compares the cost with the budget. Programmes are received and work schedules produced for the next two weeks. The labour histogram will be updated.

65. Monthly. Principle cost elements labour, plant, staff, materials, prelims, subcontractors are compared with budget on a report for site and head office management.

66. Planned and actual progress will be reported. Programmes will be reviewed and updated for the next 3 months.

67. The Buyers will produce a report which compares the value of orders placed for materials and subcontractors with the budget.

68. The Quantity Surveyors will produce a monthly valuation of work done which is compared with cash out.

69. Quarterly. The performance of all projects is reviewed at Head Office and a set of Management Accounts produced which forecast the end cost and valuation of each project. Cash flow for the business is analysed, asset useage analysed, outstanding payments noted profit earned per monthly paid employee calculated and a full written analysis of projects and the overall business produced. This report will go through to the Main plc Board.

70. The purpose of all these controls is firstly to enable early action to be taken on areas of concern, secondly to provide business information for the future planning of the business, thirdly it is the basis of feed back to the estimating teams on actual costs, the effectiveness of methods and labour outputs.

71. It is only by having a regime of standard controls reported within known time periods that the staff mobility necessary for a project based business can be achieved.

CONTRACTUAL MANAGEMENT

72. Unless the design and specification of a project is complete at the time of tender, unless quantities do not change and unless other changes for whatever reason are not introduced, then the final contract price will be different to the tender price.

73. The UK contractor today employs as many Quantity Surveyors as Engineers to ensure that he receives every penny to which he is reasonably entitled.

74. This has resulted in contractors being accused of being claim conscious, of putting profit before wanting to get on with the job.

75. The fact is that in a highly competitive market, contractors must bid keenly and then ensure that any variation to the works is properly recorded and the consequential cost recovered. On a large complex project this is a major task.

76. At tender stage, as described earlier, the Quantity Surveyor will give advice on the terms and conditions of contract and on the accuracy of the scope of works. From day one he will record and be fed information from other members of the site team regarding every change, omission or addition in the nature and scope of the works. At least one in ten of a site team will be in the QS Department.

77. Contract forms always impose on the contractor the need to give notice within set periods of delays and extra costs. Rarely is any time set for a response. It is in everyone's interest to settle claims and variations as quickly as possible. To ignore them does not remove them. Rapid resolution places more onus on the contractor to ensure he is working productively to the new budget and it helps the client know how his overall budget is moving.

FORMS OF CONTRACT

78. In the UK today we have many forms of contract and many ways in which the overall project is managed. In Civil Engineering the ICE Forms of Contract still rules supreme. It has been varied by one or two major clients such as the old CEGB.

79. Civil Engineering projects are also most likely to be carried out on a remeasured basis. The relatively straightforward nature of Civils projects has meant that the simple relationship between client, engineer and contractor has been maintained. Recently some clients, on the basis that it is their money, have sought a more active role in the agreement of extra monies. This is understandable and for contractors quite acceptable. As stated earlier, design responsibility is also being shifted towards the contractors. This is welcomed despite it meaning increased risk. The risk is offset by the opportunity to influence design and improve buildability.

80. In the building sector, traditional forms of contracting have given way, particularly in the commercial sector, to Management Contracting in all its variants. Management Contracting provides main contractors with a low return in exchange for relatively low risk. It can provide clients and their designers with more flexibility and an earlier start on site as the work is split into a series of trade packages.

81. During the last 3-4 years it has expanded as a contracting form considerably. However, the current decline in commercial development and the increasing use of

design and construct form could well mean that the use of
Management Contracting in the UK has reached its peak.
Bearing in mind the greater use of design and construct in
Europe, it is also reasonable to assume that the greater
cross fertilisation of ideas in the 90's will also promote
the growth of design and construct in the UK.  Most
individuals who have had construction work carried out for
themselves at home have horror stories to relate.  This
attitude can be found right through to the largest clients
with their mega projects.  Is it unreasonable for clients to
look for a single point of responsibility and liability?

82. The current process is generally disjointed.  Design,
development, research, construction are all separate, each
paddling his own canoe.  The future must seek to put all the
men in a single boat pulling as a team set mutually
supportive in the achievement of a single goal - client
satisfaction.

83. The organisations best able to manage this team with
the financial strength to carry risk are the contractors.
It will mean changes of attitude from everyone, not least
the contractors.

84. The challenge of Europe with the inevitable spread of
different approaches, the gradual increase in cross border
activity will add to the pressure for change.

85. Only the fittest will survive.  That is the way it
should be as anything else results in complacency and
inefficiency.  The UK contractors must and will be equal to
the challenges ahead.

# 7. Construction management and control: the experience of a French company

J. PEHUET, Vice-Chairman, GTM-Entrepose, and
J. ALLEMAND, Manager, GTM-BTP

SYNOPSIS. Using GTM-BTP, the French domestic Building and
Civil Works company of the GTM-Entrepose Group, as an example, we will attempt to develop the principles most often
used by French building and civil works contractors for the
organization and management of a construction site.

GENERAL PRINCIPLES
1.  The field of building and civil works is characterized
by the fact that each project is unique, both with respect to
the type of construction to be built and the materials and
methods used in its building and with regard to the
supervisory staff and labour to be mobilized.
2.  Furthermore, the Client, future owner of the project,
may choose various types of contract conditions

   (a)   Separate trades contract, which practically eliminates
         any possibility of subcontracting for all involved
         contractors, but which obliges the Client to employ an
         architect or an engineer to establish the project and
         coordinate the various contractors' operations during
         the progress of the works
   (b)   All trades contract, based on the architect or engi-
         neer's project ; in this case, it is the responsibi-
         lity of the main contractor firstly to execute works
         which are within its speciality and further to choose,
         either under its own responsibility, or, if specifi-
         cally
         instructed, on the Client's behalf, the subcontractors
         for remaining trades, then coordinate and control
         their works
   (c)   Turnkey contract, for which the contractor establishes
         itself the  design, with its own architects and engi-
         neers, and then performs the works under its own
         responsibility and possibly with subcontractors chosen
         by it.

3.  However, for the main contractor, whatever the type of
contract, methods and site organization are always quite
similar.

# ORGANIZATION AND IMPLEMENTATION

RELATIONS BETWEEN THE SITE AND HEAD OFFICE

4. As soon as a new contract is obtained, the company management appoints a site manager who will be responsible for managing the entire project up to acceptance by the customer and payment of all sums due. This site manager receives extensive powers from the company general management.

5. As we will see further on, he has considerable independence, enabling him to adapt his organization to the specific nature of the project on a case by case basis. However, the fact of having extensive powers does not mean that he does not need to comply with the rules in force within the company. This is particularly the case with respect to relations with the head office services at the disposal of the site. Use of these services is in some cases mandatory, and in some cases optional.

6. The site manager thus sets up a complete, independent structure on the site, adapted to the size and specific nature of the project and using the specialised services of head office when necessary.

7. <u>Design office</u>. Its assistance is essential for a turnkey contract ; furthermore it may assume special tasks for other contract types.

8. <u>Accounts Department</u>. Accounts are prepared on site which has a data processing link with the head office and are processed by the accounts departments at head office. There is a perma- nent exchange of information and results between the two structures,

9. Development of performance methods, buying, use of subcontractors, and hiring and management of labour are organized at the initiative of the site manager ; management of insurance files, management of supervisory personnel are the responsibility of the specialist services at head office. However, use of the central equipment department, the legal department or the technical design office, is at the initiative of the site manager.

10. The counterpart to this considerable independence enjoyed by the site manager is the obligation to provide precise and systematic information on financial developments on the site to the General Management of the company. With this in mind, the site manager prepares a quarterly detailed evaluation of the turnover and corresponding results obtained on a number of fixed dates, along with a quarter by quarter estimate up to the end of the project.

11. Analysis of these documents will enable the company management to intervene if it notices any major distorsions.

THE SUBCONTRACTING POLICY

12. In order to survive, a contractor must improve its performance to maintain its competitive edge. This in particular involves a permanent search for the means to improve the methods used.

13. The contractor must have teams of skilled professionals to be able to implement the methods it designs. Excessive use of subcontractors in the long run means a loss of competitiveness by the contractor. The wealth of a company is its personnel. It must therefore take care to maintain and improve the skills of its professional teams by itself performing the work for which it has the abilities.

14. The site manager will thus only resort to subcontracting in the following cases

(a) For separate trades contracts or, a fortiori, for turnkey contracts, when works are not within the abilities of the main contractor

(b) For work performed by the company occasionally and for which it has neither the supervisory staff nor the competent workers. This is, for example, the case of trades, such as painting, plumbing, electricity, on a building site

(c) To absorb temporary work overloads which are too short to warrant hiring and training new teams

15. A few major rules should be respected when the site manager searches out and selects the subcontractors : competence and availability of the teams guaranteeing compliance with both quality and delivery requirements, financial solidity of the company, satisfactory prices compatible with the allocated budget.

16. This is also valid for "all trade contracts" when a subcontractor's choice is clearly made by the contractor on the behalf of the Client.

BUYING (PROCUREMENT)

17. As we mentioned in the first chapter, the site manager is directly responsible for buying.

18. Along with the site supervisory staff, he conducts a wide-ranging consultation of suppliers and looks for the best technical and financial conditions : compliance with level of quality required, delivery dates, prices, payment conditions.

19. This decentralisation of buying to the site limits the risk of habit inherent to a centralized buying department.

20. Furthermore, the site supervisory staff's in-depth knowledge of the problem means that it is well placed to question the technical choices if the result of the supplier consultations is unsatisfactory.

SITE EQUIPMENT

21. The majority of French building and public works contractors follow a policy of ownership of their own construction plant. This is particularly the case at GTM-BTP. There is no doubt that this is positive in terms of identity of the company, of motivation of the personnel, and of management of the company, in that the equipment department has

a high capacity of adaptation to the requirements of the
various sites.

22. The site manager can then call on an equipment service
within the company. Experience has shown that he will generally resort to  it, even if he retains full freedom of
action, to call for external plant hire firms. To provide the
required service, the organization of the plant department
must therefore offer equipment which is the most appropriate
to the needs of the users, in other words, the sites and
branches.

23. Like a large number of contractors, GTM-BTP Equipment
Department is organized with a Central Equipment Service
comprising

(a) A central equipment department at head office which
buys, manages, maintains and hires to the sites all the
major plant likely to be used regularly by all the
sites run by the company (cranes, lorries, etc.)

(b) An on-site equipment distribution unit advises the
sites, records their needs and programs repairs and any
purchases needed, with one objective : to maximize and
make the most profitable use of the equipment. Constantly attentive to the remarks made by the sites and the
pricing study units within the company, it constitutes
an essential source of information for a healthy equipment renewal policy

(c) An accounts unit settles expenses, hires the equipment
out to the sites and draws up a quarterly trading
account whose balance should be close to zero. A positive trading account indicates that the equipment is
hired out at too high a cost (the works departments are
then no longer competitive) or that the equipment is
over-amortized or poorly maintained (efficiency is
liable to tail off)

(d) A buying unit bases its decisions on the needs of the
sites, on a good knowledge of the operating costs of
the machinery and on a certain volume effect

(e) A repairs centre has two main functions : storage of
plant between two sites and major interventions to
maintain the equipment

and decentralized equipment departments in each region or on
major sites which functions are twofold

(a) To act as the relay for the central plant department,
in particular with respect to routine maintenance and
possibly actual running of the equipment

(b) To buy, manage and hire to the sites the small plant
permanently assigned to the region

Their organization, albeit on a much smaller scale, is similar
to that of the central department.

QUALITY CONTROL

24. The modern notion of quality control was adopted by
GTM-BTP in 1976 for the construction of nuclear power plants.
The practical application of this notion by the personnel on
these important sites has since then been gradually extended
to several other activities within the company.

25. The quality, in a company, is a state of mind and not a
formality. It concerns organisation as much as it does technique.

26. The quality approach must be based on systematic aware-
ness : action at individual, team and company levels. This
begins with an undertaking by the General Management, leading
to executive meetings or production of a "Quality Commitment"
film intended for the personnel as a whole.

27. To achieve generalized quality procedures, the head
office Quality department, linked to the General Management,
is made available to the site managers. It thus has permanent
contacts in the regions and personnel adapted to requirements.
It instigates and combines various actions, and advises and
assists the participants in the production of the "Quality
Assurance Plans" and corresponding monitoring forms.

28. It is essential for the site management itself to
produce and then implement its own "Quality Assurance Plan",
stipulating the procedures for utilisation of resources. If
not, there is a risk of there being simply a standard plan at
head office level, one which is not actually used by those at
site level who actually implement the quality.

29. After an initial development phase in which the
creation of a "quality" approach was imposed by the project
manager, it is now increasingly frequent for it to be decided
on voluntarily by the contractor.

30. This is particularly the case with contracts combining
Design/Construction/Operation, where a continuous quality
approach to these three stages of construction is highly beneficial and thus extremely motivating for the company.

31. To date, even if complete quality control is not as
widespread as one could hope, it is at least now perceived as
essential.

CONTRACT MANAGEMENT

32. On his appointment to the head of a project, the site
manager receives from the company's price study unit a summary
of the study used to determine the sales price at the signing
of the contract.

33. A precise management framework giving him quick and
reliable information on site developments is then set up. Each
site is considered a separate entity by the head office
accounts department.

34. The first job is to set up a performance budget as soon
as the main working methods have been fixed, thus realigning
the initial price study. Within this budget, the expenditure
forecasts are broken down according to a single framework

which will also be found in the accounts and site monitoring. It also gives a detailed breakdown of the manpower allocations for each task. The quality of this document is a determining factor in quick intervention on the site after identification of expenditure.

35.   The first indicator for monitoring the site is the analysis of the manpower balance. The same applies for the consumption of the main materials (steels, concrete, etc.). These analyses of quantity rather than value are extremely simple and can be used instantly once the hours and consumption rates have been calculated.

36.   A more complete surveillance of the site is performed with the help of  accounting documents. This monthly follow-up is drawn up 10 to 15 days following the end of the month, with the back-up of the month's (m-1) analytical trading account supplied by accounts, as well as an estimate of the expenditure and budget by the site manager for month m. The accuracy of these estimations will reflect that of the result.

37.   Finally, on the basis of accounts data supplied by the accounts department and non-accounting corrections made by the site manager, an intermediate quarterly site balance is drawn up.

38.   A comparison of the results obtained with the forecasts made beforehand by the site manager will give an overall view of the site results and thus confirm or otherwise those developments identified during the monthly surveillance.

39.   These management methods, involving the site manager closely and permanently, will enable him to act with all speed to improve the performance methods and/or the resources used. They will also enable him to accurately analyse the consequences of any modifications to the contract performance conditions.

40.   Any extra work or corresponding claims will therefore have to be negotiated under his direct responsibility. In this area, he may call in advice from the company's legal department.

# Discussion on Papers 4–7

M. SMITH, <u>Swiss Federal Office of Transport, Bern, Switzerland</u>

Mr Lalaurie mentioned and emphasized the fact that the typical French client likes a lump sum contract. Does this mean that the incidence of contractors becoming insolvent is higher than elsewhere? (Apparently lump sum in France is limited to +/- 10%, i.e. it is not a lump sum in the UK context). Also, does this mean that large contractors predominate?

Mr Haensel stated that the VOB is not a legal document, but only a recommendation. What is the status of the document?

A. LEGGATT, <u>CEDIC, Farnham</u>

My experience shows different attitudes in the UK and (say) France when a problem arises on site. In the UK, the consulting engineer is called to site and the contractor takes a passive role but undertakes to carry out any instructions the engineer may give. In France, the contractor takes a positive action and is already solving the problem when the engineer arrives. The French contractor seems to feel a greater responsibility to get the job back on the rails than his British counterpart.

Of course these illustrations are very general, but I feel that they contain an underlying truth. What is the explanation? My own view is that the reason for the different attitudes lies in a combination of the differences in legal systems, roles played by the engineer, insurance arrangements etc.

P. J. DAVALL, <u>NATO HQ (Infrastructure), Brussels, Belgium</u>

Recognizing that in Germany there are now nine Laender (regions) which are autonomous with regard to construction, each having an exact, detailed, bureaucratic system for contracting work, well established regional 'family' contractors that maintain the necessary political contacts, with knowledge of local construction conditions, criteria and standards,

what advice would Dr Ing. Haensel give to foreign
contractors who wish to compete in one of these regions?

## G. HAIDER, British Waterways, Rickmansworth

'Design and construct' tenders cost a lot of money to
several tenderers.  In addition, 'lump sum' contracts
and 'design and construct' pass all the risk to the
contractor.  For taking the full risk, contractors in
Germany and France charge the client additional costs.
On the other hand, the ICE Conditions of Contract
allows only a portion of risk to be allocated to the
contractor by the client.  Would the authors agree that
on the whole, clients in Germany and France must be
paying more for the same work?  Would they agree that a
comparative study of costs for the two systems should
be carried out?

## H. A. ALLAN, Haiste International Ltd, Leeds

If I understand Mr Lalaurie's description of design
and build correctly, it is the contractor's engineer
who administers the contract and 'defends the interests
of the owner'; an interesting reversal of the UK
situation.  Even with design and build, the owner must
have had technical expertise at his disposal to prepare
the preliminary programme and bid documents and to do
the bid evaluation.  Is there any reason why the owner
would not be able to look after his own interests
through his in-house expertise or an external
consultant used at the preliminary stage?

Could the authors advise as to the usual practice in
their countries in design and build projects, where a
contractor appoints an external consultant or design
office and the bid is not successful, with regard to
payment of the consultancy fees for the abortive
preliminary design work?

## P. MCGREGOR, Export Group for the Construction Industries, London

My personal senior management experience was in heavy
engineering rather than construction, but there is a
good deal of similarity between the problems in the
construction industry and in heavy engineering, where
each order is to a new design.  Neither is really open
to pretesting of ideas in the form of prototypes, and
to that extent I disagree somewhat with John Armitt in
his written paper when he says that closer integration
will bring construction closer to the car and aeroplane
industries.  The risk inherent in the 'no prototype
factor' will continue to exist for construction, and
justifies a high contractor involvement from an early
stage; much of the risk in the others - the technical
risk as least - can be eliminated at the prototype
stage.  There will also remain for builders the vanity

factor - vanity of architect or owner's chief executive - as well as the prototype factor; we all know about buildings which win competitions but don't work, or even leak.

The allocation of risk between client and supplier has been very badly handled in Britain during the past 20-30 years. This is not just a construction problem. We have had too many clients (especially but not exclusively public sector clients) who have tended to design or heavily influence the detailed design of the product themselves rather than to set performance requirements. The end result has usually been a product which was unsaleable anywhere but in the British market, or the setting of totally uncompetitive standards. In my opinion, British public sector purchasing has done more to damage the competitiveness of British industry than any other factor one can think of. I hope the new private monopolies will do better, but I would not bet on it. The trouble is that in the end the supplier or contractor takes the real risk and the blame for any inadequacies.

The introduction of an extra party in the shape of an engineer who takes the risks of neither the client nor the contractor appears to me merely to introduce an extra dimension of problem. I have experienced enough difficulty with an in-house engineering group which considered itself to be somewhat intellectually detached from those who made the product. I can quite easily answer the point made by the British consulting engineer previously when he said that in Britain the contractor would ask him to come and say what should be done about a problem, whereas in France the contractor would get on with trying to solve it. The answer is that the British contractor would probably be correct in assuming that the problem had been created by the design consultant in the first place.

It seems to me that the separation of design and construction is just not a good idea, and its virtues are seen only by relatively simple-minded public sector purchasing officers. I have had them explain to me that to have several competing designs is a waste of money, although in any case there is such competition if there is a design competition. They are apparently unable to understand that the early interaction between the manufacturers or contractors and the designers is part of producing a competitive result, the more essential because every project is a prototype. What these people are looking for is a defensible price rather than the best price. In spite of the recent report by Reading University, there is nothing wrong with either management contracting or construction management as an alternative way of dealing with the problem of getting early construction experience into

the design, but these will only work if the client does
not try to pass on to the contractor risks which are
really his.

I cannot say that the French 'all trades' contract
appeals to me. It seems to demand a management
contractor or at least a construction manager, UK
style. In France, who carries the risks? Especially
in the large projects mentioned, which all seemed to
have public sector clients?

I was interested in the difference between the French
paper which said that 'extensive use of subcontractors
means a loss of competitiveness by a contractor', and
the British paper which still largely accepts the
continued use even of 'labour only' subcontractors or
for that matter people working as self-employed
workmen. While it seems to me that the development of
a well-managed group of qualified subcontractors would
be a sensible thing to encourage, the encouragement of
the self-employment of relatively unqualified people or
of 'labour only' subcontractors is probably in the long
run not a good idea. It even removes some value from
the design and build proposals, since the teams are not
as well established as they could be. The French paper
pointed out the importance of the teams and of their
education and training as teams. One of our real
competitive disadvantages is that we tend to lag behind
our European counterparts in the quality of our
vocational training. Great efforts have been made by
the Construction Industries Training Board, but I think
the gap remains. What is more, as is observed in Mr
Armitt's paper, these tendencies create a problem in
training first class first-line supervisors. I
remember with some wry feelings that the first
conference I ever went to on behalf of my company, a
year after I first joined industry in 1950, was on the
need to improve British first-line supervision. I was
surprised to discover when I became Industrial Director
of NEDO that from a comparison we made with the German
situation in the early 1980s, it was clear that we were
still lagging behind.

The French paper mentions that the site equipment
would be expected to be mainly owned by the
contractors, whereas in the British case it would
mainly be leased. I imagine this is probably due to
some cost advantage because of taxation rules in the UK
rather than some inherent principle. The consequences
have been unhelpful to UK construction equipment
manufacturers. Leasing companies are really only
financial intermediaries (of which we have too many in
Britain already). They don't care about the product.
Direct ownership by contractors would encourage
intelligent working between suppliers and owners to
develop better products with export potential. Another

missing piece in the tale of the British economy over
the past 30 years has been a failure to have
relationships between makers and users which resulted
in better products being developed.  This is not to ask
the users to design the product, a practice I
criticized earlier, but to enable the makers to try out
new products and obtain working experience with them.
Needless to say, this is the way the Japanese work away
at incremental improvement.

M. SMITH, Swiss Federal Office of Transport, Bern,
Switzerland
   Mr Armitt emphasizes specialization: how is one to
become a general manager?

DR M. BARNES, Coopers and Lybrand Deloitte, London
   Mr Armitt ended his presentation with a confident
statement about the place British contractors will take
in a frontierless European market, but now says that
they are unable to move into Europe due to lack of
capital.  What can be done about this?  Surely
something must be done if British contractors are even
to hold their domestic market in the longer term?

S. Y. RHYS JONES, FIDIC, London
   Following Mr Armitt's remark about his company's
policy of recruiting arts graduates for management
training, I would like to comment on one of the
difficulties faced by young engineers.  An engineering
degree course is very strenuous and highly technical,
and is followed by similar postgraduate training with
the result that few are able to maintain and/or develop
their communication skills.  Would it be worth
considering, through sponsorship or work experience,
the provision of management training?  This would not
only demonstrate to young engineers the opportunities
that lie ahead and help to encourage communication
skills, but might also encourage more graduates to
choose engineering as a career rather than moving into
other, more appealing sectors such as accounting and
management.

R. K. OLIVER, Walter Lawrence Management Ltd, Enfield
   Mr Armitt stated that construction is a risk
business: I agree, but why should the contractor accept
more risk than is implicit in any commercial
arrangement?  The risk of the unknown should be
accepted by the client - it is not beneficial to
operate in a lottery situation.  Dr Bunni stated that
projects are 'unique': again I agree, and would submit
that risk should be considered in the same light and
directed at the individual promoting the project (i.e.
the client).

# DISCUSSION

## M. BARNES, Paper 2

I have to agree to differ from Mr Oliver. Clearly, onerous subcontract conditions are sometimes the result of the imposition of non-standard clauses by the client. But in my experience particularly onerous clauses to which subcontractors rightly take objection are most often introduced by the main contractor. This is true whether the main contractor is a conventional contractor or a management contractor.

I agree with Professor Bishop's view concerning the introduction of a contract for Europe. It must be an important step towards harmonization and one which will be taken at some time in the future. The only uncertainty is whether it will be achieved within 10 years or 50. In my view, the piecemeal approach recommended by Mr Uff would be extremely lengthy and would be likely to converge upon the mediocre. An alternative, which of course has its own difficulties, would be to adopt a new contract as the European standard. The New Engineering Contract must be a candidate for consideration.

I entirely agree with Mr Barrack. Too much attention is paid to allocation of risk and not enough to shrinking risk. Many risks can be shrunk by forward thinking and forward planning by the employer in the first instance, and the employer and contractor jointly after the contract has come into existence. In my view, the first objective of designing a contract is to allocate risks so that the parties are motivated to shrink risk as much as it is within their power. All parties benefit from shrinking risks. The traditional tug-of-war of contract negotiation can be discarded once this is recognized.

## J. HAENSEL, Paper 5

In reply to Mr M. Smith, the VOB has the status of additional contractual terms which become part of the contract by written mutual agreement by the parties involved.

In reply to Mr A. Leggatt, in 'design and construct' contracts the normal case in Germany is that the engineer is a member of staff or he is a subcontractor to the construction company. Only a few years ago most construction companies held large engineering staff within their own organization. This has changed. The general attitude has not changed. The resulting engineer acts as an integral member within the contracting organization for the individual building or construction project.

In reply to Mr P. J. Davell, the most economical way to join the German market is cooperation with the local German companies, provided that their products do not interfere with each other; for example, steel contractors from outside with local contractors who are almost entirely restricted to concrete, masonry and earth-works.

As for Mr Halder's question, the German VOB requires a very detailed description of the work to be carried out. These tender documents are prepared on behalf of the client by engineers or architects. If the work is carried out fully in accordance with these tender documents the risk remains with the client. Usually, alternative design proposals are prepared by the tenderers which, if the contract is awarded, lead to 'lump sum' and 'design and construct' contracts. The risk is passed to the contractor.

Alternative design proposals are made to reduce costs relative to the clients tender design. It requires a flexible communication between consulting engineers and contractors, unlike the very rigid relationship these parties have in Great Britain. It is true that the costs of this additional design work is finally passed on as general costs to clients, but the client should profit - if the system works. A comparative study would be most helpful to decide which of the two systems should be carried out under given circumstances.

J. A. ARMITT, Paper 6
I agree with Mr McGregor that it is not possible for the construction industry process to become exactly like that of the car and aeroplane industry. However, my basic point remains that buildability and a reduction in disputes during construction will result from a closer working relationship between designer and builder at the design stage.

To add to Mr McGregor's comments on labour only subcontracting, this trend was particularly strong during the recession years of 1980-83 and reflected the need to reduce costs. In 1986-88 when the pressure was on again for quality and speed, contractors started to talk once again about the benefits of their own labour. Now we are in another recession with all the pressure on unit costs again. It is a good example of how the cyclical nature of a very competitive industry can result in fragmentation and prevents long-term developments based on continuity.

Mr Smith, I sense, sees a contradiction between specialization and the route to general management. It is not a problem as long as companies recognize that general managers require a structured development programme which builds upon the individual's particular skills. Firstly, I believe that in all countries national contractors will retain the bulk of their own market. The industry is so localized in nature, with the need to understand all the local aspects, that

DISCUSSION

local contractors will continue to dominate their
market.  For British contractors to succeed in Europe,
they must either become local in other countries
through acquisition of what become subsidiaries, or
they can joint venture on the larger projects where
they have particular skills to offer.  We still have a
series of different European markets represented by the
individual countries.

Company ownership traditions, corporate tax
structures, costs of labour, the role of the
professions are all variable.  Strategic decisions
based on recognition, understanding and acceptance of
all these issues are the first step towards becoming a
European player.

There is a continuing increase in the importance of
management as a core subject in Engineering Degrees and
thereafter as part of professional training.  It is up
to employers to encourage this trend.

A fair contract is one in which risk falls to the
party best able to make judgements of its probability
or to make qualitative judgements on how to minimize
the risk.  Where this cannot be done by a particular
party, then I would agree that the risk should be
accepted by the client.

# 8. Project financial controls

A. CRAIG, BCom, CA, MIMC, Executive Consultant, KPMG Peat
Marwick Management Consultants

SYNOPSIS. The purpose of this paper is to discuss:

- the nature of project finance, and allocation of risk amongst the major players on mega-projects, and relevant behavioural issues in the relationship between client and contractor,

- project financial controls, their nature and importance on complex projects,

- the role that an effective project cost audit can play in minimising the risk for the purchaser and in easing the communication between purchaser and contractor,

- cash flow considerations that may be appropriate on large contracts where substantial sums are being passed between client and contractor.

The paper discusses some of the reasons why many major civil engineering projects might use cost reimbursable contracts to share risk, and hence need to be able to rely on both the contractor having strong project financial controls and the purchaser having a strong project cost audit role.

## SECTION 1   PROJECT FINANCE, RISK, AND MEGA-PROJECTS

1. No discussion of project financial controls can take place without first commenting on the context in which those controls will be placed, and thus understanding the implications of the success or failure of those controls for the major players in any mega-project. I therefore commence with a discussion of the nature of project finance, and the role that allocation of risk has to play in the successful set-up and management of a project.

2. Project finance is a method of funding an enterprise based on the cash flows that the project is expected to generate. Generally it is most appropriate for projects with high capital requirements, large and complex risks, and a consequent inability to raise funds from conventional sources.

3. An increasing number of large public and private enterprises are adopting project finance because their financial requirements exceed the financing capacity of their local capital markets and of the enterprises themselves. As

traditional sources of public financing are constrained and the demand for infrastructure improvements increases, privatisation - using the skills and resources of the private sector to replace public sector enterprises - has generated additional interest in project finance.

4. Project finance is tailored to the project's economic viability and the relative reliability of its cash flows. Lenders look primarily to forecasted cash flows, rather than to project assets, as collateral for a loan. No single project is exactly like any other; rapid changes in the world's financial markets and increasing technical sophistication mean that each project finance package must be custom built.

5. Formulating the financial package for a complex project involves arranging a series of capital market instruments and structures necessary to finance the project successfully. By tailoring the cash flows and the credit support (such as completion guarantees) managers can design innovative financial approaches to meet specific project needs. Doing this normally involves addressing contractual arrangements, risk allocation, project audit, and the arrangement of cash flows, from the pre-launch right through to the post-operational phase.

6. It has been estimated that only about 20% of projects that are seriously considered are ever successfully completed. One can assume that some of the causes of this high failure rate fall into the categories of:

- delays in adoption and completion (with consequent delays in the anticipated revenue flow),

- technical failures,

- poor management, and

- legislative or political changes.

7. Typically, there is an irreducible minimum of intrinsic risk in a project - risk that has to be managed. The allocation of the various risks to those participants best able to manage them will reduce a project's overall risk. Indeed, allocation of risk on a mega-project can be likened to a diversification strategy - and the key to successful project financing is to identify and manage those risks appropriately.

8. After all, no one has found a way of abolishing risk. It is all around us. Risks change too - today the risks you and I run are more likely to be concerned with the consequences of failing to maintain competitive advantage, failing to anticipate redundancy of our own skills as the world changes at a faster and faster rate. Some parts of our world economy thrive on the management and insurance of risk. Other parts, such as the construction industry, are trying to become very good at avoiding risk - contractors in particular shuffle risk about so that as much of it as possible sticks on their purchasers!

9. Recent news of sizeable overruns on the costs of major construction projects around the world has reminded us again of risk in relation to mega-projects. Some of the best case studies of risk in mega-projects have occurred

in recent years here in the UK, and I would select the AGR nuclear power station programme, the Thames Flood Barrier and the Channel Tunnel Fixed Link as three of the most interesting. I have had these three very different types of project very much in mind whilst writing this paper; I shall draw on aspects of them as I discuss the context of the risks they shared between purchaser and contractor, the project financial controls in place, and the role played by project audit of the costs.

10. The Thames Barrier provides a good example of construction and labour relations risk, and how the purchaser, the old GLC, was unable to insulate itself from the construction and financial risks of the project. When tenders were invited for the civil engineering works it was found that no contractor would enter into a contract without an escape route for him to turn to if he made unacceptable losses. After five years of work, the contract was re-written, converting it to a cost reimbursable basis but with attractive incentives to the contractor for completion on time and within a target cost. It is vital to note that once the contractor had terms which would give him a good return for effort, and shelter him from risk, the project was delivered on time and on cost.

11. It is seldom necessary for a whole contract to be written on a cost reimbursable basis. The skilful contracts officer will divide the project up into manageable components - his diversification strategy - and only let contracts on a reimbursable basis for those parts of the total job where the risks cannot be measured or are too large to be acceptable to contractors. The rest he will let on an alternative basis suitable in the circumstances. For example, there might be difficult design problems to be overcome before the construction phase begins. In these circumstances it may be appropriate to let a cost reimbursable design contract, with a break so that the actual construction work is done on a measured work basis.

12. It is always most interesting to study the behavioural implications for senior construction management of incentive payments earned by contractors for achieving targets and, at the opposite extreme, penalties suffered by contractors for late completion. It is a common if not universal feature of conventional construction contracts to include a liquidated damages clause providing for late completion. Purchasers often rely on such clauses as a stick to beat a contractor into performance. If a purchaser has this as his intention when entering into a contract for an intrinsically high risk project, then he seriously misjudges human behaviour. In the final analysis the behaviour and attitudes of the contractor's senior management are critical to the interests not only of the contractor but also of the purchaser. On a mega-project huge prizes can be won if the senior management of the supplier and the purchaser are pulling in the same direction.

13. I have observed the visible changes in senior contractor's staff motivation where, on the introduction of target incentives, they perceived an identity of interest with the purchaser and because of this they were injected with a powerful motivation. A large and unusually long and risky civil engineering contract which was let for the Thames Barrier on a conventional basis reached a situation, in mid-term, of running into serious delays. This was causing serious demoralisation of the senior staff of the contractor and an unusually productive "claims industry". The contractor began to adopt a risk minimisation strategy

which was in sharp conflict with the purchaser's need to accelerate the programme. The divergence of interest between the aims of the contractor and the purchaser had become total. And if a contractor is so threatened by loss he adopts a risk minimisation strategy, the interests of the purchaser have flown out of the window.

14. When the contract in question was renegotiated to a target contract the change in motivation of the contractor's staff was electric. Clearly, improved performance arose from creating an atmosphere of identity of interest between the contractor and the purchaser. The behavioural lesson should be learned - it delivered the project by the newly agreed date at the newly agreed cost.

15. The criteria by which the purchaser will assess his contract strategy will be by reference to the relative importance to him of time, cost and quality. An assessment needs to be made by the purchaser of the contractor's ability to achieve a performance which will affect either time, cost or quality, and the design of any target contract or target element can concentrate on giving the contractor an incentive to perform in the area required by the purchaser, coupled with controls over the less crucial variables. If the incentive is to have any impact on the contract outcome the target must be achievable and perceived by the contractor to be significant in amount.

16. I have been involved in the AGR nuclear power station programme, and also in the latter stages of the Thames Barrier programme; in both these cases the purchaser and the supplier were, at least by the end of the project, pulling in the same direction. The results, whilst not without the usual difficulties over settling the final numbers, and in the case of the Thames Barrier, a contract renegotiation, were successful projects achieved on time and very close to budget - and achieved in something much closer to a spirit of harmony than is commonly the case.

17. More recently, it has also been fascinating to be involved in the current Channel Tunnel Fixed Link construction project. The combination of the size of the undertaking - the largest civil engineering project in Europe - and the overall complexity of the project would be enough to challenge the most experienced project managers. We shall all watch with interest as the project nears completion in the next few years.

18. Interestingly, one of the interesting aspects of this project has been the additional dimension of its UK/France interface. Everyone involved in the project has underestimated the impact of the international communication that is necessary - including ourselves! It is not enough simply to double any estimates; I speculate that the extent of the extra work involved is a geometric progression, wherever more than one country is involved. I would like to suggest to anyone contemplating a multi-national project, particularly where two or more languages could be used, that you double your estimates of international communications costs and interaction - and then double them again!

## SECTION 2   PROJECT FINANCIAL CONTROLS

19.   Having chosen the type of contract that is appropriate for the risks involved and the situation, it is important to consider the project financial controls that should operate.

20.   I would propose that the contractor's project financial controls need to be rigorous on any major contract, regardless of whether the contract has been let on a lump sum basis or a cost reimbursement basis. The contractor must have suitable financial controls and monitoring mechanisms in place at every level. A project that is well managed in its financial disciplines will in turn generate an atmosphere of accountability and responsibility in all other aspects.

21.   It has been suggested in the past, and held up as an argument against the use of cost reimbursable contracts, that the contractor is only interested in proper financial controls if it is a lump sum contract, and not at all interested if it is a reimbursable contract. Similarly the converse is held to be true for the purchaser, who is held to only be interested in a contractor's financial controls if it is a cost reimbursable contract.

22.   Whilst I understand why this view is held, I disagree with it. In my opinion it disregards both the power of the mutuality of interest discussed in paragraph 12 above, and the subtleties that can be achieved in project management under cost reimbursable contracts where this common interest in the successful outcome of the contract is in place. It is my experience that the contractor is capable of being just as keen to impose proper financial controls on his work as the purchaser, not only as part and parcel of the harmonious relationship, but for the very real commercial reason that both stand to gain handsomely if costs really can be controlled.

23.   In speaking to contractors as part of my independent project cost audit role, I have never had to persuade their senior management of the benefits available to them if financial controls are tight - they want the rigorous discipline to be in place just as much as I do on behalf of my client.

24.   The key to getting effective project financial controls in place is what every MBA student in every management school is taught - management, management, management. You can have as good a financial control and reporting system as you wish, and pay substantial sums of money for it, but if the implementation of the system, the enforcement of the necessary disciplines, and the will of management to see it through, are not there, it is of no use in controlling costs or influencing performance throughout the project.

25.   Project financial controls - in any organisation, but particularly on a one-off mega-project of significant complexity - depend heavily on having the right management in place. It comes down to having:

- an effective leader in charge of the organisation from the very start,

- a top management team who are actually working as a team, and

- effective control systems to control and monitor the costs and the performance throughout the project.

26. Communication is crucial between the owner and the contractor, at the appropriate levels, to ensure that the required structure of both parties' management is right for the particular project in hand, and to ensure that each side understands the other's structure sufficiently to establish the "lateral" communication links as effectively as the "vertical" links within their own organisations.

27. In many project situations this extends to having complementary systems that allow details of costs and progress to be relayed electronically via common or interfacing project control systems. This project reporting area is where perhaps the most useful technological improvements have been made in the last 5 to 10 years. With the advent of a personal computer on every manager's desk, which can be linked into minicomputer or mainframe databases, and where what were once complex calculations of performance indices and inflation adjustments can now be performed in seconds at the keyboard, has changed the working lives of many of us. Major breakthroughs have also been made in information technology in the construction field that make automated time-clocking, automated production control, and computer aided design available to owners and contractors alike. Any large project that is being considered in the 1990's must consider taking advantage of these improvements - traditional methods of hand-cranking our familiar manual systems are just not appropriate any more.

28. It is indeed one of the challenges that is facing the industry today - to harness the power of the technology to do not only what we already do (but faster and more reliably) but also to develop new ways of working that enhance our ability to control projects.

## SECTION 3   PROJECT COST AUDIT

29. This discussion of project financial controls leads me on to ask the question: who makes sure these controls are in place?

30. The construction industry is full of stories, some improved significantly by the telling and retelling in the bar afterwards, of individuals successfully circumnavigating project financial and procedural controls for their own gain. Indeed, in any commercial undertaking there is bound to be a bit of "flexibility" in certain quarters, even if only on the claiming of travelling and subsistence expenses!

31. Issues include failures in the correct application of the contractor's procedures as laid down, of which the contractor himself was not aware. These are remarkably common, especially on mega-projects where the sheer scope and the number of interfaces involved make it extremely difficult for anyone, with the best of intentions, to control all aspects. Examples include:

- authorisation by senior contractor management not properly obtained,

- authorisation by client not properly obtained,

- proliferation of "fast track" ordering, avoiding the normal procedures,

- insufficient care over the proper allocation of overheads and common costs between contracts,

- insufficient computer security procedures, or poor data back-up facilities.

32. Secondly, the cost audit can identify minor fiddles (which can of course develop into major difficulties if not stamped out swiftly) perpetrated by more or less senior members of the contractor's staff, including:

- deliveries of materials to other projects or addresses,

- "dead men" on the reimbursable payroll,

- credits due to the reimbursable contract being received by other (lump sum) contracts,

- payments made on account to subcontractors not being recognised against the subsequent invoice for the work, effectively duplicating payment,

- supposedly fixed assets "walking",

- arranged tendering, or possibly duplicate invoicing, by a "related" company who is also a subcontractor.

33. There are numerous other examples, the only limits being the imagination of the perpetrator, the vigilance of the senior management - and the experience of the auditor!

34. Under cost reimbursable target cost type contracts, particularly those where there is one part of the works under a cost reimbursable contract and another under a fixed price contract, there is considerable scope for the contractor to slip costs into the reimbursable accounts that might properly be attributable to the fixed price contract or other unrelated contracts.

35. In these circumstances it is essential for the project as a whole to have a measure of audit of the costs. It is also desirable that the organisation carrying out the audit of the contractor's costs under the cost reimbursable contract be independent from both the purchaser and the contractor. This is where my own experience lies - in the audit of major cost reimbursable contracts on behalf of the purchaser and with the full cooperation of the contractor.

36. This last point - the full cooperation of the contractor - cannot be stressed enough; no stick taken to a contractor will be effective if there is not a mutuality of interest between the purchaser and the contractor. Not even the engagement of an international audit and consultancy firm experienced in the audit of contract costs in a cost reimbursable environment can solve all your problems! The contractor's senior management must welcome the advice and assistance that can be given to him by the auditor, appreciating that it is the interests of both his client and himself that the most efficient controls are in place.

37. I believe that project cost audit can contribute in a number of ways. Firstly an experienced project auditor can assist in the setting up of suitable controlling and monitoring procedures from the start of the contract, which will ensure that "best practice" is in place for both purchaser and contractor. Financial management and computing techniques can be added to the unique mix of skills that any project management team will already encompass; a measure of independent advice in the early stages is seldom inappropriate, as the key players may already be to close to the project to be able to see the wood for the trees.

38. Later in the project, during the construction phase, the experienced project auditor can contribute by checking that the costs have been reasonably and properly incurred, and by the independent monitoring of the cost control procedures.

39. Some of the issues identified in paragraphs 31 and 32 above are relatively "common sense", and an experienced construction eye on site, with access to the books and records of the contractor to cross check his suspicions, would be able to pick up a number of anomalies on the average contract. However some aspects of the work involve large volumes of data to be checked (such as the routine checking of perhaps thousands of purchase order invoices) and sophisticated audit sampling techniques are called for. Equally, the more complex issues such as the computer security and data back-up require the specialist expertise of computer consultants to assess the risks of significant loss and the adequacy of the procedures adopted by the contractor.

40. I would maintain that an accounting firm's audit method is extremely useful in suggesting a selection of possible tests to be carried out and a rigorous approach to quantifying the results. However it is in itself insufficient unless backed up with the "nose" of the experienced auditor who knows the industry and understands the people in that industry. It is important to use only staff and techniques for the cost audit that are appropriate to that contract; the project cost audit role on a major contract demands a construction-experienced consultant to handle the negotiations between client and contractor - someone who understands the industry and the people in it very well.

41. My experience of the audit of the three major projects mentioned in paragraph 9 above has encompassed a range of techniques to identify the particular problems the contractor might be having, given his unique situation and the purchaser's unique set of perceived risks and requirements. Particularly in the early stages of the AGR nuclear power station programme and the Thames Barrier work, I have used relatively simple but exceedingly rigorous techniques, involving a large invoice-checking element. I have also advocated sophisticated sampling and analysis techniques designed to minimise the "ticking" and increases the flexibility to explore different risk areas as the project develops.

42. On occasion, the development of the tailored approaches has stretched the minds of my colleagues in our international audit practice! The complexities of auditing a highly dynamic project with no year-ends and quite different objectives invalidates a number of the normal "statutory audit" assumptions, and of course the volumes of transactions to be checked can be significantly greater. The approach to be adopted on any particular project depends on the

objectives of the purchaser, the complexity of the contract, the volumes of transactions to be checked, and the relative riskiness attributed to the various cost areas.

43. The type of work carried out by project cost audit mirrors what is done in a statutory audit of a company's books, but it has a vital difference - it is not aimed at assessing whether a "true and fair view" has been shown in a set of financial statements, but at a giving "comfort" to the purchaser (and the financiers of the purchaser) that "management" is managing; that the costs incurred really do relate to the work that has been carried out, the right controls are in place, and the costs as stated by the contractor should be reimbursed.

44. Because of this difference in objectives, the approach is somewhat different for contract cost audit - the transactions are tested in greater depth, the cost coding can be crucial, and the work can be focused to concentrate on particular risks at particular times in the course of one contract. For instance, proper authorisation of commitments in the early stages, the allocation of costs to different parts of the contract during the peak of the construction phase, and the control of claims and releases of retentions towards the end of the contract.

45. In addition, on a statutory audit physical presence of audit staff is likely to consist of a twice-yearly relatively brief visit to the subject's offices. By contrast, the physical presence for long periods on site during the performance of the contract can be a valuable influence on the contractor's behaviour, as well as enabling the audit staff to become closely familiar with the actual work being carried out. There is nothing quite like "walking the job", and the experienced project auditor will make use of this.

46. In auditing the costs on the project we are essentially looking at two aspects of the contractor's performance:

- his adherence to proper control procedures, and

- his actual costs which are ultimately intended for reimbursement.

47. These two aspects are tested through two different but related auditing mechanisms:

- "compliance" testing of the contractor's procedures - for example, were the purchase order and subsequent invoice properly authorised?

- "substantive" testing of the costs - for example, is the invoice for goods that have been properly received, does it add up, were the goods invoiced for only once, is it addressed to the right contractor, is it coded to the right part of the job, and any other tests that are relevant to that type of cost.

48. One could just use substantive testing alone, and check a large proportion of all transactions in order to gain comfort that the costs are reasonably and properly incurred. However there are two main advantages of combining both approaches. Firstly, if reliance can be placed on a system or procedure through compliance testing, then fewer of the transactions going through that procedure need be tested to obtain the same level of "comfort". Secondly, any poor procedures that the contractor is operating can be identified. There may not necessarily be a cost implication directly, but, in my experience, for all the reasons stated already in this paper, the contractor will welcome constructive suggestions for ways in which improvements could be made to his controls.

49. It is important to recognise that the "attest" function being outlined here is certifying that the cost has been properly accounted for under the terms of the contract between the purchaser and the supplier; it is not giving a technical, engineering or commercial comment on the expenditure, nor commenting on the quality of the work done for that cost. These functions need to take place alongside the cost audit function, and the results coordinated at a senior level to ensure that all aspects are properly covered.

50. This coordination is where the really effective owner/client will be able to use the financial knowledge gained in the cost audit work to help assess the cost implications of any deficiencies found in the technical aspects of the work, and will be able to apply significant pressure on the contractor to perform better.

## SECTION 4   CASH FLOW CONSIDERATIONS

51. I would like to add another dimension to the discussion so far, which is also related to the use of cost reimbursable contracts on mega-projects. Once the purchaser has established that he will only be paying that which he rightly ought to pay under the contract, an additional concern is how he will hand over the cash to the contractor. He will wish to achieve this in such a way that the contractor doesn't get his hands on money that he should not, or too early, and earn interest on that extra cash that rightly would belong to the purchaser.

52. From the contractor's point of view, it is essential that he is assured of continuing cash flow, and able to pay his suppliers and employees appropriately. He should, after all, be concentrating on managing the project effectively, and his time is better spent on, for instance, generating meaningful cash flow forecasts, rather than being held up in his work by continual wranglings with his employer over the mechanics of the cash flows.

53. We have found that a useful method of satisfying both parties involves transferring the cash from one to the other on an "automatic" basis, administered through the banking system, but only funding those amounts that have actually left the contractor's separate contract bank account that day. Thus the contractor is not holding any cash even overnight, yet he is sure of always having his cheques honoured.

54. This whole process is then monitored as part of the audit work outlined in paragraphs 29 to 50 above, to ensure that the payments the contractor is making are indeed related to that cost reimbursable contract, and are not, for instance, being made unreasonably early to related companies of the contractor.

55. At any time during the course of the contract and of course at the conclusion, a reconciliation can be made between the cash spent via the bank accounts versus the costs incurred in the books.

56. Of course, it is perfectly possible to continue to pay the contractor weekly or monthly on smaller projects; indeed even large projects adopting the method described above may wish to revert to a weekly call-down against listed invoices (and take the higher exposure to interest rates) towards the end of a contract, when the volume of transactions is small and the value diminishing rapidly to just the settlement of final claims. But the "open book" on the contractor's bank statements still provides the purchaser with the necessary comfort that he is not transferring the cash out of his own hard-pressed bank account without due care and redress.

57. During the course of the audit, it is likely that a number of anomalies and errors will arise. After all, no contractor is perfect, and if the project cost audit is functioning effectively there will be a number of issues raised which have been agreed with the contractor and resolved, and also a number of queries outstanding for further discussion. It is essential that these are resolved as quickly as possible in order to keep the contract moving ahead smoothly; as they are resolved then the books of the contractor are adjusted accordingly and redress can be made for monies paid out that are deemed not to be for reimbursement, and a notional interest charge calculated.

58. The simplicity of the transfer of cash, the openness of the records, the scrutiny by external accountancy-trained audit personnel, and the resulting calm, factual statement of the position between the parties regarding the cash flows, greatly assists the maintenance of a reasonable and rational relationship between the parties.

SECTION 5   SUMMARY

59. I firstly discussed the nature of project finance, and issue of the allocation of risk amongst the major players on mega-projects. I considered the importance of the behavioural issues that are at stake in managing those risks, and the role that properly structured cost reimbursable target contracts can play in generating a identity of interest and purpose between owner and contractor.

60. I then considered the nature of project financial controls and their importance on major projects, and focused on the importance of leadership and the management team as well as tight project controls.

61. I then discussed the role that an effective project cost audit could play, described some of the range of techniques that can be brought to bear, and outlined the advantages of having an independent monitor of the financial situation and of the procedures in place.

62. Lastly I proffered some considerations in the area of managing the cash flows between owner and contractor during a typical large construction project.

# 10. Legal liabilities in construction in Europe

## V. VAN HOUTTE, Partner, Stibbe & Blaisse & De Jong

SYNOPSIS. The creation of an Internal Market for
construction activities will expose the construction
industry and professionals to liabilities which are
different from those in their country of origin. These
rules may override contractual arrangements agreed between
the parties and as a result could therefore deter industry
and professionals from construction activities abroad. This
barrier to trade and to the free movement of services is one
reason for the EC Commission to harmonize the rules on
professional liability in construction. The protection of
the "consumer" of the construction industry is another.

INTRODUCTION - THE EUROPEAN CONSTRUCTION MARKET
1. The European construction industry has an annual
turnover estimated at more than 500 billion ECU. Its
economic importance is thus comparable to that of the
agricultural sector, which is much more visible in the EC's
activities. The EC is now forcing open the market for
public construction contracts by means of a variety of
measures :
- the recent improvement of the works' directive
  (Directive 89/440/EEC, O.J. L 210/1, July 21, 1989),
- the adoption of the so-called "remedies directive"
  (Directive 89/665/EEC, O.J. L 395/33, December 30,
  1989),
- the extension of the principle of European-wide
  competition to the so-called "excluded sectors" namely
  water, energy, transport and the telecommunications
  (Amended proposal for directive, O.J. C 264/22, October
  16, 1989 with a separate proposal on remedies, O.J. C
  216/8, August 31, 1990) and even,
- the extension of the public procurement rules to
  services, obliging architects and consulting engineers
  among others to compete internationally for projects
  involving fees of at least 400,000 ECU (proposal not yet
  published) and even to services in the "excluded
  sectors" (preliminary draft).

The opening-up of the market for public works and services
will internationalize not only the public sector of the
construction market, but, as a secondary effect, also the
private sector.

2.   The EC already has taken numerous other measures which
will contribute towards this liberalization :
-   the Directive on Construction Materials (directive
    89/106/EEC, O.J. L 40/12, February 11, 1989) aims to
    ensure the free movement of construction materials in
    the Common Market and to stimulate technical
    harmonization.
-   Eurocodes are under preparation which lay down rules for
    the design of structures in different types of projects
    or methods of construction.
-   the Directive on Recognition of Diplomas and Free
    Establishment in the field of Architecture opens the way
    for international architects' practice (Directive
    85/384/EEC, O.J. L 223/15, August 21, 1985).
-   a list of vocational qualifications in construction
    removes the barriers which national technical
    qualifications constituted for foreign construction
    technicians (O.J. C 292, November 20, 1989).

3.   No matter how encompassing the EC's technical
harmonization effort, allowing the professions and the
industry to work abroad under the same technical terms as in
their home country, they will, for some time to come, face
other differences of a more legal nature which may be quite
disturbing if unprepared for.

LEGAL LIABILITIES

4.   The title of this paper is in fact a pleonasm.
According to the Oxford American Dictionary, "liability"
means "being liable" which in turn is defined as "being held
responsible by law". The title might thus be more
accurately stated as "legal responsibilities" as opposed to
"moral responsibilities".
Not every moral responsibility carries with it a legal
liability and a legal responsibility does not always imply a
moral responsibility.  English speakers in fact are lucky,
because they have two words in their vocabulary to
distinguish the two notions :
- responsibility and
- liability.
The French have to make do with the single term
"responsabilité".

5.   Responsibility is always related to a fault, omission
or negligence.
Liability on the other hand is often the result of
responsibility.  In all cases, however, where the liability
is not fault- or negligence-related, there is no question of
responsibility but rather of risk (ref. 1). The so-called
"strict" liability or, as the French call it,
"responsabilité objective" or "responsabilité de plein

droit" has nothing to do with responsibility but everything
to do with an allocation of risk, which the legislator or
the courts put on a specific party's or group's shoulders.
This allocation may be based on the economic strength of one
group, on its capability to control, or at least to
influence the risk, on pragmatic reasons such as relative
facility of insurance of the risk or the number of risk
cases which the group meets.
   6.  If, on the eve of the opening of the doors of the
European Market, legal liabilities in Europe are a worry to
the construction industry and professions, this is precisely
because legal liability does not coincide with
responsibility.  Practicing abroad would not give rise to
the same degree of concern if the only rule were that one is
liable whenever he is responsible, i.e. has been negligent.
Every practicioner would then know the extent of his
exposure.
However, legal systems where one is liable, even when not
negligent, or where one is not liable (after a period of
time, or for certain types of defects), even though the
defect is caused by one's own negligence, are uncomfortable
to work in unless one is familiar with these legal
intricacies.  The way in which the legislator or the courts
have allocated the risks, i.e. the liability which does not
sanction negligence, depends on a number of local social and
other reasons and, hence, differ from country to country.

NATIONAL VARIETY
   7.  At the request of the EC Commission, Mr. Mathurin, a
French engineer, has undertaken a comparative study of the
legal environment for construction in each EC member state.
He has described the contractual structures commonly used in
each country, as well as the controls to which construction
activities are subject, the liabilities and the available
insurance.
From his report, the Commission has concluded that "few
countries have truly satisfactory legal systems" and that
"loopholes, uncertainties, complications and divergences
abound" (Commission Working Document on Possible Action to
be taken on the Study of Responsibilities, Guarantees and
Insurance in the Construction Industry with a view to
Harmonization at Community Level, 1990, p. 4).
   8.  The statement applies without distinction to countries
with civil law and common law traditions.  The practice in
the latter to "distinguish" one case from another always
leaves open the possibility that the next case may not be
decided along the lines of the existing precedent.  Code
law, for its part, cannot provide solutions for all
practical problems and is necessarily complemented by court
decisions which do not even have the status of a
"precedent".

Different interpretations of the same code articles are possible, especially when comparing different national jurisdictions. For example, article 1645 of the Dutch Civil Code and article 1792 of the Belgian Civil Code contain the same rule of decennial liability for the structural integrity of the building. Yet, these articles are interpreted differently by the courts of both countries : the decennial liability is considered to be an issue of public policy and cannot be restricted in scope or in time by the parties. In the Netherlands, both the level and the duration of the liability of contractors, architects and engineers can be validly limited, through use of the professions' general conditions of employment.
It is evident that such situations can play nasty tricks on people who are unfamiliar with the local rules and that every party to a construction contract with transnational aspects should be aware of the differences.

9. The differences which merit closest attention, are those created by rules which relate to matters considered to be of public policy.
At least in construction contracts with private clients, the rule of contractual freedom of the parties applies as a principle, meaning that the parties are free to agree on their respective rights and obligations in relation to each other. The legislator tends to restrict this freedom when it appears that one of the parties is often the weaker party and needs legislative protection against the stronger party. Hence, for example, the Belgian statute of July 9, 1971 on the construction of private residential buildings restricts parties' contractual freedom considerably in order to protect the owner against certain abuses by contractors.

WHICH NATIONAL LAW IS APPLICABLE TO AN INTERNATIONAL CONSTRUCTION CONTRACT ?

10. When the project is located in one country and the owner, architect, engineer, contractor and financier come from different countries, the law of each of these countries may be applicable to their contracts. Parties may, as part of their contractual freedom, choose any of these national laws as the applicable law.
If no explicit choice of law is made, the court or arbitral tribunal which is competent to settle the dispute, must first determine the applicable law. This can either be the law which the parties have chosen implicitly or the law which has the strongest links with the contract. The "strongest link" refers to the criterion of the place where the "most characteristic obligation" under the contract is to be performed.
For a contractor, this is generally the place where the project is built. For a consulting engineer involved exclusively in design, it may be the place where the design is made, that is, in his home country.

11.   Construction rules which are considered to govern
issues of public policy are applicable locally : thus, a
project or a contract is always governed by the public
policy rules in force in the country where the project is
located.

Tortious liability, as a rule, is governed by the law of the
country in which the tort occurs.  In practice, this
generally means the country in which the damage occurs.
For transboundary projects (for example the Channel Tunnel),
this means that they may be governed (at least in part) by
more than one system of national law.

CONTRACTUAL LIABILITY - TORTIOUS LIABILITY

12.   Contractual liability is the liability a party to a
contract has towards its contract partner for
non-performance of a contractual obligation.  Tortious
liability is the liability for damages, as a result of
injury caused by one's negligence.  The same concepts exist
on the continent where tortious liability is called
"responsabilité civile" or "quasi-délictuelle".

Tortious liability and contractual liability are subject to
different rules : contractual negligence may or may not be
tortious negligence; the damage to be indemnified may not be
the same when it is caused by a tort rather than a breach of
contract; the statute of limitations applicable to each may
be different, etc...

13.   Tortious liability has been applied extensively in
the United Kingdom by extending the circle of beneficiaries
of the duty of care.  As a result, third parties, who had no
contractual link with a party to a building contract, have
been able to claim damages for infringement by such party of
its contractual obligations.  Even contract partners have
occasionally been allowed to sue each other in tort, instead
of in contract - which had the advantage of evading
contractual clauses restricting liability or even statutory
limitation periods.

14.   On the continent, attempts for a similar extension of
tort liability have been made.  In Belgium for one, such
attempts have met with only limited success.

First of all, there is the theory that a party to a contract
can sue its partner only in contract.  Only third parties
can be sued in tort.  An action in tort between contract
partners is admitted only if the negligence which was
committed, is not an infringement of a contractual
obligation and if the damage suffered is not a contractual
damage.

As a result, a client cannot normally sue his contractor in
tort.

Secondly, the Belgian Supreme Court has held that the person
to whom a party has delegated the performance of part of his
own contract, for example a subcontractor, is an agent of
the main contractor and therefore not a true third party to
the client.  Consequently, the above rule that only third

parties can be sued in tort, applies also to subcontractors : they cannot be sued in tort, unless their negligence and the ensuing damage is non-contractual.
For example, when a welder-subcontractor as a result of his negligence, caused a fire in the plant where he was performing his contractual obligations, he was held liable in tort to the owner - with whom he had no contract - because he committed a breach of his general duty of care - different from any contractual duty he had - which caused damage other than damage following from failure to perform his contract.
The combination of the two rules often lead to situations where a client has no action at all against a subcontractor : he is restricted in an action concerning the negligence of a subcontractor to an action in contract against the main contractor who in turn can sue the subcontractor.
The "collateral warranty" from a subcontractor for the benefit of the client is not yet familiar in continental practice.

LIABILITY OF THE ENGINEER WITH REGARD TO THE CONTRACTOR
   15.   When the engineer is appointed directly by the client, design errors of the engineer cause damage for the contractor.
In English law, it seems accepted now that the contractor does not have a direct action for damages against the engineer.  The latter is considered the agent of the client and his negligence can thus be attributed to the client who must indemnify the contractor for damages caused.  The client of course can subsequently have recourse against the engineer (ref. 2).
   16.   On the continent, the question is to be answered on basis of the principle of "responsabilité civile" or "quasi-délictuelle".  Under this rule, anyone who causes damage to another person by his neglicence, has to indemnify that person for any injury suffered.  The victim of the negligence has to prove :
1. that there was negligence
2. that he suffered damage, and
3. that the damage was caused by the negligence.
The difficult question here is whether the breach of a contractual obligation owed to a contract partner may constitute a tort vis-à-vis a third party to the contract.
   17.   In France, cases exist where this question has been answered positively.
In Italy, the possibility for a direct claim in tort by a contractor against the engineer seems to exist in theory, but there appear to be hardly any cases where the engineer has actually been condemned since the burden of proof on the contractor is rather heavy.
In Germany, there are no cases of liability of the engineer towards the contractor except where the engineer was found

to be jointly liable with the contractor vis-à-vis the
owner. In such a case, when the contractor was sued by the
client, the contractor can sue the engineer to ensure that
he intervenes in the procedure, and then disclaim liability
for that part of the damage which was caused by the
contributory negligence of the engineer.

INFLUENCE OF CONTRACTUAL RELATIONSHIPS
18. As professional liability in construction is in the
first place contractual liability, it is clear that the
structure of the contractual relationship is a determining
factor in settling the issue of liability.
These structures show a wide range of possible variations on
the traditional triangle of the so-called "Infernal Trio" of
employer, engineer and contractor. Still, certain
structures appear to be more traditional in some countries
than in others (ref. 3).
For Anglo-Saxon practitioners, it is important to know that
the continental engineer does not traditionally hold the
same position as his Anglo-Saxon counterpart. The "Code
Napoléon" used the term "architect" to designate the
professional in charge of the design of the project as
opposed to the contractor who constructs the project.
Although the engineer's technical role in design is in
practice probably as important on the continent as in the
United Kingdom, and although the engineer is subject to the
continental decennial liability to the same extent as the
architect and the contractor, the engineer's role has not
otherwise received the same legal recognition on the
continent as that of the architect.
19. On the contrary, the 1936 and 1962 Belgian statutes
have given Belgian architects a monopoly for the design of
all construction projects requiring a building permit, and
for the control of the construction activities. In France,
architects hold the same monopoly for buildings.
This explains why Belgian engineers very often have no
direct contract with the owner, but work in fact as
subcontractors for the architect, even for projects where
the technical aspects prevail over the architectural ones.
20. As a result, the question of whether the owner has a
direct action against a sub-contractor has been raised in
Belgium quite frequently in connection with the liability of
an engineer towards the owner, when the engineer had been
hired by the architect. This has led the Belgian courts to
find a solution for the conflict between the legal monopoly
of architects on the one hand, and the technical
developments in construction on the other. As a result of
these developments, architects are no longer competent in
practice to take charge of the entire design of a project.
While the architect is supposed to be fully liable towards
the owner for defects in his design and in the design
prepared by his subcontractors (the engineers), the courts
have nevertheless realized that it has become impossible in

practice for architects to be knowledgeable as to all technical developments to the extent that they are in a position to control the design work made by their subcontractors - engineers.

A decision of the Belgian Supreme Court of 1978 has concluded that,

"given the high technicality of certain construction studies, the architect is authorized to exonerate himself, even implicitly, vis-à-vis his client, from any liability with regard to the technical studies such as the structural studies, for which he has not been trained and which are therefore not within his competence".

The Supreme Court added, however, that the architect would still be liable if it appeared that the choice of the engineer whom he had appointed was clearly a bad choice or if the error committed by the specialized engineer was of such a nature that the professional knowledge of the architect should have allowed him to discover it.

21. The allocation of contractual obligations of course also influences the liability of the parties. For example, although the architect has a monopoly for the design of projects under Belgian law, in practice he has the possibility to assign part of that design responsibility to the contractor. In fact, the architect very often prepares the general terms and conditions for the construction contract, and may in this way impose certain design obligations on the contractor. Although the design activities performed by the contractors are normally restricted to so-called "execution design", it frequently happens that conceptual design activities are also transferred to the contractor in this way.

JOINT AND SEVERAL LIABILITY

22. Joint and several liability normally exists only when the parties have jointly subscribed to a single contractual obligation towards a client. For example, a consortium of contractors having jointly undertaken to construct a project, are jointly liable towards the owner for its defects. Architects and contractors do not normally undertake such joint obligations with regard to a client. This would only be the case for example when the architect and contractor cooperate as a joint venture for the performance of a turn key contract. Consequently, when architect and contractor have separate contracts with the owner which require separate performances from each of them, they should normally not be jointly liable for damages suffered by the owner as a result of the negligent performance by either one of them.

23. Still, the courts in Belgium and France have created a special in solidum liability which is an entirely jurisprudential construction.

Its origins are to be found in the increase in the number of builders simultaneously engaged on a construction site,

which sometimes makes it difficult to allocate exactly the
liability for each specific defect or each specific error.
Moreover, the courts consider that builders have a duty of
mutual supervision of each other's performances : a
contractor should not restrict himself to slavishly
following only those plans which he receives from the
architect or the engineer.  On the other hand, the
architect/engineer has also a duty to control the
construction by the contractor.  The result of this duty of
mutual control is very often that for a single error on the
site, at least two persons may be liable : the person who
committed the error and the person who presumably ought to
have noticed it.

24.   The rule of mutual control leads to situations where
parties often seem to be liable for the errors of others.
In Belgium and France, the architect/engineer is frequently
held in solidum liable with the contractor for what was
originally a defective performance entirely on the part of
the contractor.  All too often, the courts when seeing a
faulty performance by the contractor, jump to the conclusion
that the architect, who by law is obliged to control the
construction activities of the contractor, has been
negligent in performing his duty of control.

The in solidum liability means that the owner is entitled to
claim 100 % of the damages from either of the two parties
condemned in solidum.  After payment, either of these
parties has recourse against the other party for contribution up to the amount which is supposedly due to the specific fault of that party.  Very often, however, it so happens
that one of the two parties is not solvent, which means that
the other party is left with the indemnification of the
total damage.  In this way builders involved in a project,
although they have no contract with each other and have not
even chosen to work with each other, may find them- selves
to be the guarantor of not only the professional competence
of the other parties, but even of their financial solvency.

## "OBLIGATION DE MOYEN" - "OBLIGATION DE RESULTAT"

25.   With regard to professional liability, the
Napoleontic countries distinguish between an "obligation de
moyen", on the one hand, and an "obligation de résultat", on
the other hand.  In case of breach of a duty of care ("obligation de moyen"), the burden of proof lies with the client.
The mere fact that the project has a defect, does not show
that the builder has been negligent.  If the obligation
assumed by the builder is one for a specific result,
however, the mere non-compliance of the project with the
guaranteed result will constitute evidence of negligence on
the part of the builder.  In such a case, the builder has
the burden of proof to show that the alleged defect resulted
from a specific cause other than his negligence.  Whether an
obligation contained in a construction contract is an
"obligation de moyen" or an "obligation de résultat" depends

on the type of obligation and the way in which it has been expressed. In general, it would appear that professionals generally assume "obligations de moyen", whereas many obligations of contractors are generally "obligations de résultat".

JURISDICTION
   26.  Most legal systems authorize the parties to a construction contract to agree on the jurisdiction for disputes.
International contracts generally provide for arbitration, since they are often performed in developing countries to whose jurisdiction the Western contractors or funders of the project prefer not to be submitted (see e.g. the arbitration clause in the new general conditions for work contracts of the European Development Fund and the draft Arbitration Rules of the EDF).
The completion of the unified Internal European Market will lead to an increase in the number of international construction contracts in the EC, and consequently the choice of jurisdiction shall become a frequent issue, even for less "exotic" projects.
In this respect, however, the EC countries have different traditions.  Arbitration of construction disputes is common and frequent in Denmark, Ireland, the Netherlands and the United Kingdom but is rare in the other member states, although there is an increasing trend towards arbitration in Germany and Italy, as a result of overburdened courts.
The success of construction arbitration in certain countries can be explained, at least in part, by the widespread use of standardized general conditions of contract containing an arbitration clause (e.g. UAR and UAV in the Netherlands, AB in Denmark, VOB in Germany).
Arbitration in construction contracts is particular, however, in that many construction disputes are multipartite.  The organization of multipartite arbitrations is still relatively complex.  For example, in the Netherlands the arbitration law has been amended quite recently in order to provide specifically for multipartite arbitrations.  Still, the newly created possibility to join arbitration cases, is used extremely rarely.  Thus, the Dutch tradition is pursued to have construction disputes handled by three different arbitration institutes (one for the client-architect contract, one for the client-engineer contract and one for the client-contractor contract).  This system often creates inconsistent decisions from different arbitration institutes and often means double procedures for one or two parties.
   27.  The creation of European-wide common rules for dispute settlement in construction has been proposed from several sides during the investigation which the EC Commission has launched on responsibilities, guarantees and insurance in the European construction sector.

In general, it would appear that those countries which have specialized construction arbitration are the most satisfied with their local system.

PROFESSIONAL LIABILITY INSURANCE

28.   Insurance is increasingly considered to be an adequate solution to liability problems in the construction industry.   Thus, several national legislators have made insurance mandatory for one or more of the parties to construction contracts.

In France, the so-called "Spinetta" statute requires two insurances : one liability insurance and one object-insurance.   Anyone who could be held liable, according to the presumption contained in articles 1792 and ff CC, for the construction of buildings, is obliged by law, on sanction of certain penalties, to insure his liability each time a new project is started (PII).   In addition, the client himself must take out insurance for damage to the building.   This policy covers him against the risk that none of the builders are eventually held liable (the so-called "liability-gap") and against the risk that, in the event of a finding of liability, much time would elapse before the client obtains recovery of his damages (the so-called "time-gap").   Thus, the client's insurance allows him to have the damage repaired immediately, without having to await the outcome of the liability dispute.   Repair is made at the expenses of the insurer, who has recourse against one or more of the builders' insurers.

According to the Spinetta statute, the manufacturer of defective components or equipment for a building is jointly liable with the contractor, even when the manufacturer is established and produces outside France.   Consequently, foreign contractors and suppliers for building projects located in France, are subject to the same rules, not only on liability but also on insurance.

29.   In an international contract, the question arises whether foreign contractors, who must insure their decennial liability for a French construction project, can take out such insurance in their own country.   In this respect, the French statute provides only that the insured must be able to prove that his insurance cover complies with the statute. Therefore, a German contractor can in theory participate in a French project under the cover of his German insurance policy, provided it extends to France.   In practice, however, it may not be certain that the German insurer in fact covers the risks in accordance with the French statute. It will therefore be easier for the German contractor to comply with the requirements of the Spinetta statute, if he takes out insurance from a French company which is familiar with the local construction liability legislation.

The German contractor may be handicapped vis-à-vis his French competitor, however, when he takes out French insurance : he probably has less references or security in France and may have to pay higher premiums. In this way, national rules imposing mandatory insurance constitute a barrier to the freedom of professionals from other EC member states to provide services.

30. A similar situation exists in Belgium where since spring 1985 architects have been obliged by law to carry professional liability insurance. The 1985 EC directive on freedom of establishment and services in the field of architecture provides in Article 25 that, if a country makes professional liability insurance mandatory, an insurance certificate delivered by the architect's country of origin has to be accepted as equivalent to the receiving country's own certificates. The certificate must state that the insurer has complied, as regards the nature and scope of the coverage, with the legal requirements of the host member state. Query, however, whether, until the realization of a single European insurance market, insurers in one country will be interested in covering specific risks which only exist abroad and with which they may not be familiar.

HARMONIZATION OF LIABILITY RULES BY THE EEC

31. As already mentioned before, the EC Commission, prompted by its own White Paper of June 1985 and by the resolution of the European Parliament of October 12, 1989 on the need for Community action in the field of construction, has launched a vast study of the possibilities of harmonizing the liability rules in construction throughout the EC. Mr. Caronna will talk hereafter of the status and the prospects of this work. We shall restrict ourselves in this paper to a short enumeration of the various measures which have already been adopted in the past by the EC Commission which may influence the liability of builders.

The 1985 directive on product liability (Directive 85/374/EEC, O.J. L 210/89, August 7, 1985)

32. This directive introduced the rule of strict liability of a producer for damage caused by a defective product. The directive is also applicable to moveables which are incorporated in an immoveable, such as construction materials in the broad sense. Nevertheless, the directive is of concern not only to manufacturers of construction materials, but also to contractors. In fact, the directive provides that when the producer of a product cannot be identified, each supplier of the product shall be treated as its producer unless he informs the injured person within a reasonable time of the identity of the producer or of the person who supplied him with the product. Consequently, contractors shall fall within the ambit of the directive in their capacity of "supplier". For example, a client may have a direct claim against the subcontractor who incorporated a defective product which he cannot trace back to the supplier.

100

The 1988 directive on construction materials

33.   Although its aim is to achieve the free movement of
construction materials in the Common Market and to stimulate
technical harmonization, the directive of December 21, 1988
(O.J. L 40/12, February 11, 1989) may have a considerable
impact on construction liability.  It requires construction
materials to have certain characteristics so that the
construction projects in which they will ultimately be
incorporated, satisfy the essential requirements listed in
Annex I to the directive concerning :
- stability,
- fire-safety,
- hygiene, health and environment,
- use-safety,
- noise-protection,
- energy economy and heat retention.
34.   While these essential requirements no doubt are
already part of standard good workmanship rules of European
designers and contractors, they raise two questions :
i)  Subject to normal maintenance, these requirements must
    be satisfied throughout the duration of an "economically
    reasonable working life".  What is the relationship
    between this vague expression and the various periods of
    construction liability?
ii) What is the relationship between these six "essential
    requirements" of the directive and the "serious defects"
    in construction works which, in the national legislation
    of various member states render their authors liable for
    longer periods (e.g. decennial liability).  So far, a
    distinction has been drawn between, on the one hand,
    defects affecting the stability or fitness for purpose
    of the building or construction project, and, on the
    other hand, the so-called minor defects, which e.g. in
    France, are equipment-defects (for which the liability
    period is much shorter).
    However, the "essential requirements" list now contains
    items such as energy economy and noise protection which
    until today were not likely to be considered "serious"
    defects.  The existence of Annex I may well influence
    the national courts and legislators when assessing the
    seriousness of certain defects and corresponding
    liability.

Draft directive on liability for services with a safety
defect

35.   This draft is, in the field of services, roughly the
equivalent of the product liability directive of 1985.
Thus, it creates strict liability for the supplier of a
service.  The services related to design or construction of
immoveable property were originally included in the
preliminary draft for this directive, which even provided
longer liability periods for construction-related services

than for other services. Also in view of DG III's ongoing
work on harmonization of the liability rules,
construction-related services are now entirely excluded from
this draft directive.

Draft directive on safety of products

The draft directive on minimal requirements for security and
health on mobile worksites

CONCLUSION

36. The above examples of Community legislative action
bearing - if only indirectly - on professional liability in
construction, indicate that the Commission has foremost the
protection of the consumer in mind. The consumers of the
construction industry are not a homogenous group, however.
The consumer is certainly the client, but also the public at
large. Moreover, the client is not always a naive and
inexperienced owner who is the weaker party in the
construction contract. On the contrary, many clients are
professional developpers, certainly in no need of special
legislative protection.

37. In these circumstances, it seems improper to put all
the risks which are involved in construction, on the
construction industry and professionals. An increase of the
cost of construction, defensive design, withdrawal from
certain markets will certainly follow from an unbalanced
risk allocation.

38. We therefore argue that strict liability must be
rejected and that only the rule of liability in case of
proven negligence is to be maintained.
Even so, it would appear that this liability should be
- limited
  . in time, and
  . in amount
- contractual, to the exclusion of tortious liability,
- individual and in no case joint and several.
Despite the fact that these limitations are necessary for
the professional side, the remaining risks may nevertheless
prove too heavy for clients or consumers. Availability of
insurance for their own risks should be guaranteed, at a
reasonable cost. The insurance of projects by clients will
ensure that the client sees the direct relationship between
the quality and safety he expects from his projects and
their cost.

REFERENCES

1. VAN HOUTTE V. Risk in construction : Damages which are not caused by negligence, Building Research and Practice, 1988, 352-355.

2. DUNCAN WALLACE I. Charter for the Construction Professional, Construction Law Journal, 1990, 207 & ff.

3. WISHART I. Building in the European Communities, Construction Law Journal, 1990, 3-6.

# 11. Insurance

N. G. BUNNI, BSc, MSc, PhD, FICE, FIEI, FIStructE, FCIArb, and
T. J. O'CONNOR (International) Ltd

SYNOPSIS. Insurance is needed for many aspects of the
construction project to safeguard the promoter, professionals,
contractors, and third parties. These aspects depend on a
large matrix of risks which are inherent in the construction
process. Many risks, if they eventuate, could lead to
liabilities of enormous magnitude. Indemnity through
insurance is arranged in different jurisdictions in various
ways during construction of the project and after its
completion. These are discussed and analysed.

## HAZARDS AND RISKS IN CONSTRUCTION

1. It is accepted that exposure to hazards and risks in
the work environment is highest in the construction fields
of activity (ref. 1). These risks are traditionally shared
between the parties involved in construction in accordance
with the provisions of two contracts usually agreed: firstly
between the promoter and the design professionals involved;
and secondly between the promoter and the main contractor
From the latter agreement, where the promoter is referred to
as the Employer, flows another line of risk sharing between
the main contractor and sub-contractors, suppliers,
manufacturers, insurers and others.

2. If these risks are analysed on the basis of their
effect, two basic types of risk can be identified. The first
type incorporates the risks which could lead to damage or
injury if they eventuate. The second incorporates the risks
which could lead to either action or in-action with the
consequences of either non-payment or delay in completion
and/or a cost over-run of the construction project. Figure
1 shows a classification of the risk in construction and
the manner in which they are generally shared in the contract
between the employer and the contractor. It also shows the
role of the insurance in providing indemnity when such risks
eventuate.

3. Examples of the first type of risk are: defective
design, defective material, defective workmanship, Acts of
God, fire, etc. Examples of the second type are: late
possession of the site, delay in receipt of information
necessary for timely construction, changes in design,

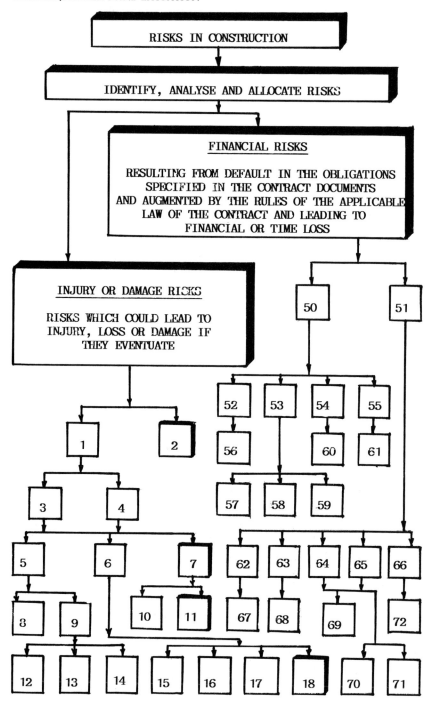

## KEY TO THE NUMBERS GIVEN IN FIGURE 1

1 : Employer's Risks (Specified)
2 : Contractor's Risks (All others)
3 : Special Risks
4 : Normal Risks
5 : Required to be insured under the Contract
6 : Insurable risks but not required to be insured under
the Contract.
7 : Un-insurable by the insurance market
8 : By self insurance
9 : By an insurer
10: Liability of Employer
11: Liability of Contractor
12: C.A.R., Contractors All Risks insurance
13: P.L., Public Liability insurance
14: E.L., Employer's liability insurance
15: P.I., Professional indemnity insurance for Engineers
and Contractor
16: P.L., Public liability insurance for Employer
17: E.L., Employer's liability insurance for Employer
18: D.I.C., Difference-In-Conditions insurance including
non-negligence


50: Employer's Risks
51: Contractor's Risks
52: Delay in Performance by Employer and cost over-run
53: Faulty design by Engineer & negligence of other
professionals
54: Non-performance
55: Delay in Performance by Contractor & related costs
56: Un-insurable
57: Professional indemnity insurance (limited in amount)
58: Project insurance (limited in time)
59: Decennial insurance (limited in scope)
60: Performance security
61: Completion Risk insurance
62: Delay in Performance
63: Additional Costs
64: Defects
65: Latent Defects
66: Non-performance
67: Un-insurable
68: Un-insurable
69: Decennial insurance
70: Defective material and workmanship (sometimes insurable)
71: Public liabilities including those for defective design
and construction

variations etc. (ref. 2).

4.　In this connection, three principles must be kept in mind.　These are:

  (a)The meaning and significance of "Risk";

  (b)Not all undesirable events can be perceived and identified; and

  (c)Whilst risks generally imply undesirable events and consequences, in certain circumstances desirable as well as undesirable consequences may occur (ref. 3).

5.　It is necessary to elaborate on the first principle. Risk is defined in British Standard No. 4778, 1979, as the combined effect of the probability of occurrence of an undesirable event, and the magnitude of the event.　It is therefore a measure of the combined effect of the probability and the intensity of a hazard (the undesirable event being referred to as hazard).　Mathematically, the relationship may be represented by the following expression:

$$Risk = Hazard \times Probability\ of\ occurrence$$

The hazard is measured in terms of severity and intensity and is classified in the British standard No. 4778 into four categories:

  (a)negligible;

  (b)controlled or marginal;

  (c)critical;

  (d)catastrophic.

6.　This classification is based on the effect produced once the hazard occurs and may include any one or a combination of the following consequences: loss of life; personal injury; damage to reputation; material damage; financial loss; loss of time; and mental distress.　Therefore, it is usually assumed that a catastrophic hazard would result in loss of life, personal injury, mental distress, financial loss, physical or tangible damage and loss of time; a critical hazard would result in personal injury, mental distress, material damage, financial loss and loss of time requiring immediate attention to prevent further damage; a marginal hazard would result in financial loss, loss of time and malfunction that could be corrected; a neglibible hazard would result in only slight damage which could be disregarded.

7.　The severity and intensity may be expressed along a scale based on the above grading starting at zero and ending at any fixed figure of say 10 or 100.　The probability of occurrence may also be expressed in such terms of a set scale or statistically in terms of the likelihood of the event (ref. 4). It is to be noted that when considering the acceptability of a particular risk, the severity of the hazard and its probability of occurrence should be considered simultaneously.　Thus, a high severity combined with a low probability of occurrence may lead to an acceptable risk whilst a low severity with a very high probability may be unacceptable.

8. If and when risks eventuate, liabilities may flow in accordance with two principles:
  (a)The provisions of the applicable law of the Contract which differ from one jurisdiction to another as described by Mrs. Vera Van Houtte in her paper on the legal liabilities under the different legal systems; and
  (b)The manner in which these risks and the resultant liabilities are allocated under the Contract or Contracts between the Parties.

## SHARING OF RISKS

9. Traditionally, allocation of the risks and legal liabilities between the parties in a construction contract is shared on the basis of the obligations and duties assigned to each of them. The obligations and duties in such a project are extremely complex and one need only look at any standard conditions of contract to realise the extent of this complexity. Amongst these standard conditions are:
  (a)The I.C.E. Conditions of Contract for Works of Civil Engineering Construction in the U.K.;
  (b)The Joint Contract Tribunal for building work in the U.K.;
  (c)The Verdingungs Ordnung für Bauleistungen in Germany;
  (d)The Het Algemene Lastenkohier of Cahier des Charges in Belgium;
  (e)The Uniforme Administratieve Voorwaarden in the Netherlands;
  (f)The I.E.I. Conditions of Contract for Works of Civil Engineering Works in Ireland;
  (g)Articles of Agreement and Schedule of Conditions of the Royal Institute of the Architects of Ireland for building works.
  (h)The FIDIC Conditions of Contract for Works of Civil Engineering Construction and also for Electrical and Mechanical Works.
  (i)The EDF General Conditions of Contract for Works Contracts.
  (j)others

10. As the matrix of risk becomes larger, the number of variables increases and the need for risk management becomes evident. It is also obvious that as the construction project becomes larger, its complexity increases and the need for using computers and sophisticated software for risk management becomes more obvious. Such programmes exist and have been used (ref. 5).

11. When liabilities arise in a construction project, the best course for covering them is by providing indemnities through insurance. This is due to some specific characteristics unique to the Construction project. These are:
  (a)The Contractor must complete the Contract, irrespective of the occurrence of any undesirable events or some other deterrents;

(b)Construction projects involve vast sums of money frequently provided by banks, financial institutions and insurance companies which require some form of guarantee as to the safety of the capital they provide for financing the project.

(c)No two projects are alike.

(d)Hazards and risks exist in numerous categories and numbers.

(e)Analysis of tenders is made easier if a simple figure (through insurance premium) is included in respect of liabilities which might be incurred by the Contractor. See reference 3 above.

12.   However, not all risks are insurable and some which are insurable can be either extremely costly or inappropriate to insure.   Figure 1 showed the available insurance covers for the indemnities which may be activated once risks eventuate but these are not always required to be issued under the provisions of the Standard Contract.   On the one extreme the Contract may call for no insurance whatsoever whilst on the other a variety of insurance policies are required.

## INSURANCE

13.   The insurances available irrespective of the requirement of the Contract may be divided into two categories:   Firstly, the insurances which can be arranged during the construction period; and secondly those which can be arranged after substantial completion of the Works and "Taking Over" by the Employer.

14.   The first category includes the following:

(a)Insurance of the Works, materials and machinery, apparatus and such similar plant intended to form part of the Permanent Works.   The Employer should be jointly insured under this cover.

(b)Insurance of the Contractor's Equipment, machinery and appliances required for the execution and completion of the Works.   The Employer should be jointly insured under this cover.

(c)Insurance against any liability of the Contractor for death of or injury to any person, other than workmen in the employment of the Contractor, or loss of or damage to any property, other than the Works or property of the workmen.   The Employer should be jointly insured under this cover.   The sum insured may however be limited.

(d)Insurance against any liability of the Contractor for or in respect of any damages or compensation payable to any person in the employment of the Contractor.

(e)Insurance against any liability of the Employer for or in respect of any damages or compensation payable to any person in the employment of the Employer.

(f)Insurance against public liability of the Employer from any act or default of the Employer, his agents or servants.

(g)Professional indemnity insurance in respect of any
design carried out for the works, whether Permanent or
Temporary. This cover is usually obtained by the
party entrusted with the design.

(h)Difference-In-Conditions insurance for any gap between
risks insured under the above insurance covers and
the Employer's Risks as specified in the Contract.

(i)Professional indemnity insurance in respect of any
service provided by professional advisers engaged
on the project, other than design.

(j)"Completion Risk" insurance in respect of the Employer's
risks of additional delay costs which are the direct
result of factors beyond his control (such as physical
damage, technical non-performance, delay by contractor
or supplier, force majeure, ground conditions, weather
conditions and changes in the applicable law of the
Contract).

15.   The second category of insurances incorporates those
available after substatial completion of the Works.  They
include the following:

(a)Continuation of the insurances described in items (a)
to (h) in paragraph 14 above for the duration of the
Defects Liability Period.

(b)Project insurance which is sometimes obtainable for the
whole project after substantial completion and for a
limited period of time of between three and five
years.  This insurance cover is usually negotiated for
each project individually and can be regarded as an all
embracing cover for the risks to which the project is
exposed including the faulty design, material and
workmanship.

(c)Decennial insurance for a period of ten years from
the date of substantial completion of the Works to
cover latent defects, essentially for commercial,
industrial, public buildings and only some civil
engineering Works which contain a high proportion
of structural engineering elements such as bridges
or water towers.

16.   The insurance covers and policies issued in respect of
the items described in paragraphs 14 and 15 above are well
known to most of those involved in construction.  The
limitation imposed on the length of this paper prevents any
further elaborations.  In any case many references exist, see
reference 4 above for further information.  For decennial
insurance, however, some relevant information is given below.

## DECENNIAL INSURANCE

17.   Decennial insurance was originally designed as a cover
against the decennial liability imposed by law in some
countries such as France, where the liability is known as
"responsabilite decennale", and also in many of the Middle
East countries.  Article 1792 of the 1979 French Civil Code
which deals with the topic of decennial liability provides:

"Every constructor of a structure is legally
responsible to the owner or those deriving title
from him for any damage (including damage
resulting from sub-soil conditions) which
jeopardises the integrity of the structure or
which by affecting one of its component elements
or one of the equipment elements renders the
structure unfit for its intended purpose.

Such responsibility will not be imposed where
the builder demonstrates that the said damage
results from causation outside his authority
and control."

The article classifies in its sub-articles the definition
of "constructor". Articles 2270 and 2820 deal with the ten
year period of liability and the insurances required by
law in respect of this liability, respectively. The
provisions of Article 2820 of the French Civil Code are
not common amongst other jurisdictions.

18. The essential features of decennial insurance may
be briefly summarised as follows (ref. 6):

(a) Decennial insurance is a non-cancellable material
damage or threat of damage insurance cover against
specified latent defects which threaten the stability
and strength of a structure and also against physical
damage resulting from such defects in design, materials
and construction. Other risks covered by standard
policies such as fire are not covered by this insurance.

(b) Although the cover is usually limited to the structure
it may be extended to the weathershield envelope and
to subsidence, heave or land slip producing or
threatening structural damage. The cover may also
be extended to include the cost of removal of stock,
machinery, plant, fittings or furniture whilst repair
work is carried out following an insured damage.
Temporary storage costs can also be included if the
sum insured is correctly calculated. Where business
interruption insurance or financial consequential
loss is required, it can be obtained under an annual
seperate policy.

(c) The cost of dismantling and partial demolition of
any part of the building may also be part of the
cover.

(d) Loss of rent is an optional extra and when granted it
is usually subjected to an excess of one month with a
maximum of two years.

(e) The protection under decennial insurance is for ten
years starting from the date of practical completion.

(f) The policy is negotiated by the Owner or developer
before or during the preliminary stages of design.

(g) The sum insured is either the "full value" of the
building or a "first loss" value chosen by the owner
or dictated by the insurance market capacity. Both
sums may be indexed. As the normal basis of Claims

Settlement is the Full Reinstatment of the damaged
or lost item, a Full Value Sum Insured should
represent the total estimated cost of re-building the
Premises, including a provision for demolition and
Debris Removal as well as Professional Fees
(Architects's Engineer's Legal etc).

If a First Loss sum insured is chosen, the Insured is,
of course, responsible for the residue.

(h) As with most property damage insurances the decennial
insurance policy is "Subject to Average" which reduces
the amount of a claim in proportion to any amount of
under insurance.    Indexation should avoid the
problem of under insurance.   Furthermore, it is
usually possible to "Top-up" the Sum Insured during
the period of insurance if inflation rises faster than
expected, subject to an appropriate additional premium.

Decennial insurance provides for indexation either on
the basis of an agreed level of inflation which is
automatically added periodically or on the basis that
the insured would top up premiums to maintain full
value cover.

(i) The decennial insurance policy is assignable to
successive owners.

(j) The inclusive insurance premium for decennial cover is
generally within the range of 0.8% to 2.5% of the
full replacement value depending on the severity of
the risk. It is usually paid in two stages, the first
payment of between 40% and 50% of the total amount
is paid at the end of the preliminary design stage;
the balance being due at the date of practical completion
when the Insurer is first at risk.   In most cases the
minimum amount of premium for a policy is around £5000.
Therefore, projects less than £250,000 may be
considered outside this type of insurance.   Premium
rates for small projects are generally higher than for
large projects.   This is mainly because inspection
fees cost around the same for both and also because
defects costing about £150,000 are most common, in
both large and small projects.   However, there are
many more rating factors that affect the level of
premium required and these include:-

(a)   The type of building and its intended usuage;
(b)   the type of construction and its foundations;
(c)   the project location and geological factors;
(d)   the amounts of indexation and deductible selected;
(e)   the first loss sum insured (if any);
(f)   weather proofing cover if required;
(g)   other extensions to the cover;
(h)   Status of developer, contractor, architect,
engineer; etc.

(k) Decennial insurace provides, at an additional premium
for a waiver of insurers' subrogation rights against
the Insured's professional team, thus creating a

no-fault policy with the one exception : that of a contractor's responsibility for correcting defects arising during the contractual defects liability period.

(1)There is also a deductible specified at a level which imposes a discipline on the conduct of the Insured and the professional team. A deductible of £10,000 is not unusual. The deductible may also be indexed in line with the sum insured in order to keep pace with inflation.

(m)Risk assessment and management during the stages of design and construction is undertaken by independent consultants appointed by the Insurer, referred to as the Technical Control Agency. It is this assessment of the risk that permits premiums to be kept to a minimum by making sure that only projects that are economically acceptable are covered, or that high risk projects are subject to an additional premium. This is very similar to the surveys conducted for other classes of insurance like fire, theft, engineering, etc. It is very important that specialists identify the areas of risk of inherent defects, because unlike other material damage policies of insurance this Ten Year Policy is a "once and for all" NON-CANCELLABLE COMMITMENT once cover has started. Risk control is not intended of course to duplicate the design or supervisory role of the architect or consulting engineer on the project.

19. The technical control services in decennial insurance include:

(a)The checking of drawings and technical documents;
(b)Periodic site inspection during construction; and
(c)Quality control of materials.

## PERFORMANCE SECURITY

20. Performance securities can be provided through insurance. Therefore, although not strictly an insurance cover, it has to be included under the topic of insurances (ref. 7).

## DIFFERENT REQUIREMENTS IN DIFFERENT JURISDICTIONS

21. Insurance requirements differ from one country to another and from one jurisdiction to another. Decennial insurance is required by law in France. I understand that the standard Dutch Contractor's All Risks insurance policy includes for latent defects liabilities for a period of ten years after substantial completion (ref. 8). In some European countries the Standard Conditions of Contract do not call for any insurances to be issued, and so on. Further information on these differences would be of particular interest to those interested in unifying the European approach to construction and to re-structuring liability and indemnity in the European Community. Some work has already been initiated in this context, by the International

Council for Building Research, CIB, set up in 1985. Its
Working Commission W87, for Post-construction liability and
insurance brings together the experience from more than 13
countries. (ref. 9).

Mr. Claude Mathurin of Agence Qualite Construction, Paris,
was commissioned in the Autumn of 1987 to carry out a research
project for the European Community dealing with the areas of
liability, insurance, guarantee, survey/inspection, and
Conditions of Contract, but the information compiled is
perhaps not sufficient to provide a comprehensive picture
on this topic. (ref. 10).

## REFERENCES

1. Health and Safety Executive, Health and Safety Statistics
published periodically by the Government Statistical Service,
Her Majesty's Stationery Office (H.M.S.O.).
2. BUNNI N.G. Constrution, Insurance and Law. Forensic
Engineering, The International Journal, Third International
Conference on Structural Failure, Product Liability and
Technical Insurance, Vienna, July, 1989, Pergannon Press, 1990.
3. BUNNI N.G. The FIDIC Contract. A book to be published by
Blackwell Scientific Publishers Ltd., Osney Mead, Oxford,
OX2 OEL, England, In April, 1991.
4. BUNNI N.G. Construction Insurance. p.33. Elsevier Applied
Science Publishers, London, 1986.
5. Hayes R.W. and Perry J.G., Thompson P.A. and Willmer G.
Risk Management in Engineering Construction. Thomas Telford
Ltd., London, 1986.
6. BUNNI N.G. Decennial Insurance and The Effect of I.S.O.
9000 on Quality Assurance. The Structures and Construction
Section of the Institution of Engineers of Ireland, Dublin
1989.
7. BUNNI N.G. Bonds, Securities and Insurance. Euro-
Conferences, Copenhagen and London, 1988.
8. Atkins Planning Report on Latent Defects in Buildings: An
analysis of insurance possibilities, page 54, September, 1985.
9. Atkinson G. Insurance against latent defects: Some major
international developments. Structural Survey, Volume 7, No.
1, London, 1988.
10. Mathurin C. Study of Responsibilities, Guarantees and
Insurance in the Construction Industry with a view to
harmonisation at Community level, Brussels, February, 1990.

# 12. Construction dispute settlement in the European Single Market

M. E. SCHNEIDER, Lalive Budin and Partners

SYNOPSIS. A great variety of procedures and institutions exist in Europe to assist the parties to a construction contract in avoiding or settling disputes during the performance of the work or after completion (part 1). In some larger projects overseas and, exceptionally, in Europe, mechanisms and rules have been adopted to provide for efficient disputes settlement prior to arbitration or court proceedings (part 2). Action to harmonize and coordinate dispute settlement procedures in Europe might best commence by an inventory of existing domestic procedures and institutions, and by efforts to adapt them to work in a European context; specific attention should be paid to the development of a European system for urgent decisions during the performance of the work (part 3).

## 1. THE PRINCIPAL FORMS OF DISPUTE SETTLEMENT IN A COMPARATIVE VIEW

Dispute settlement mechanisms differ considerably from one European country to another; within each country the rules and practices for disputes with the Government and other public authorities often differ from those applicable to private contracts. There are, however, also a number of common features between several countries. Such common features may be due to common legal traditions or to the particular requirements of the construction industry.

Rather than describing the systems prevailing in each country, one after the other, it appeared preferable to identify the principal forms and mechanisms for dispute settlement and to describe their application in the major legal systems in the Community.

## 1.1 Dispute settlement in the course of contract administration (agreement between the parties or management by the Engineer or the maître d'oeuvre)

The construction of civil engineering and building works requires a multitude of activities by different trades performed not on the premisses of the contractor but on a construction site which normally belongs to the employer. At numerous instances, interfaces occur between the work of the contractor and the contributions which the employer, or other contractors retained by him, have to make. The type and number of these interfaces vary according to the type of contract: they differ for instance between a turnkey lump-sum contract on the one hand and a project with multiple contractors and remeasurement contract. In all contracts, however, an important amount of management and coordination is necessary.

There are two basic approaches possible with respect to this management and coordination. On the one hand, the parties may attempt to allocate between the contractor and the employer as clearly as possible their respective responsibilities and related management activities: the German VOB is a good example of this approach. On the other hand, one may entrust a third person, more or less independent of one or the other party to the contract, with contract administration and management of the interfaces; this system has been developed in England since the nineteenth century, has been exported to other common law countries and, through the FIDIC Civil Engineering Conditions, to many other countries especially in the Third World.

In this originally English system - which in the present author's opinion provides a particularly ingenious solution to a complex problem - the architect or engineer plays a central role in contract administration and certification; this role includes important functions in dispute avoidance and settlement. This may be illustrated by a few examples from the ICE Conditions:

The Engineer has powers

- to "explain and adjust" any "ambiguities or divergences" in the contract documents (Clause 5) and may grant an extension of time and compensation for additional costs related thereto (Clause 13 (3);

- to decide that "exceptional adverse weather conditions or other special circumstances of any kind whatsoever be such as to fairly entitle the Contractor to an extension of time...";

-   to decide whether adverse physical conditions or artificial obstructions entitle the Contractor to an extension of time or compensation for additional costs (Clause 12);

-   to " ascertain and determine by admeasurement the value in accordance with the work done..." (Clause 56 (1);

-   to decide on the amount due to the Contractor on account of his monthly statements and to issue interim certificates to this effect which the Employer must pay (Clause 60);

These powers enable the Engineer to settle differences as and when they arise and often, in situations of potential conflict, make it possible for him, to prevent a dispute from arising.

In order to understand the system correctly, it must be pointed out, however, that, in the interpretation which English courts have given to these and similar powers of engineers and architects, the engineer does not settle a dispute about contractual rights and obligations but exercises his discretion to complete the contract on behalf of the parties.[1] In the point of view of English lawyers, matters of "extension of time, liquidated damages, recovery of loss or expense, valuations of variations and so on"[2] are not clearly regulated in the contract and form part of the "elements of fluidity"[3] which are so prominent in construction contracts. The mechanisms of English construction contracts which give to the architect or engineer powers to make decisions in these matters, in the eyes of English law, do not concern the settlement of disputes about contractual rights and obligations but a "specified machinery to establish an obligation".[4]

As a result of this conception, the decisions of the architect or engineer in these matters cannot be reviewed by

---

[1] See e.g. LLOYD in ICLR (1988) pp 330 seq.

[2] BINGHAM L.J. in the Court of Appeal in Ashville Investments Ltd. v. Elmer Contractors Limited (1987) 37 BLR 55 at 79

[3] ibid p 78

[4] Northern Regional Health Authority v. Derek Crouch Construction Limited (1984) 26 BLR 1 at 29 as per Browne-Wilkinson L.J., emphasis added

the courts, except in cases of bad faith or excess of power.[5] Under English law, it is therefore vitally important for the parties, if they wish an arbitrator to review the engineer's decision, to include in the arbitration clause a provision which gives to the arbitrator "full power to open up review and revise any decision opinion instruction directions certificate or valuation of the Engineer".[6]

Thus, when opening up or reviewing the engineer's decisions and replacing them by his own decisions, the English arbitrator is seen as acting, like the engineer, to establish an obligation on behalf of the parties.

For a lawyer from the European continent, the English approach may appear surprising. In the areas described, the engineer and the arbitrator make decisions which, under continental contract practice, are likely to be considered acts to clarify and complete already existing contractual obligations. Therefore, such decisions could be made and reviewed by the courts. From a comparative point of view, these decisions under English contract conditions therefore may well be characterized as a form of dispute settlement.

The approach opposite to that of the English style of contract administration may be illustrated by the German VOB. Instead of reserving areas of "fluidity" which the engineer or architect crystallizes by decisions and certificates using his discretion, the VOB tries to settle matters directly between the two parties to the contract. In Germany, as elsewhere, the employer frequently retains architects or other professionals to assist him in the performance of the work. But in the contractual relationship, in particular as regulated by the VOB/B they appear only as his agents.

The VOB[7] identifies interfaces and situations where

---

[5] ibid. The situation would be similar in Germany, i.e. the courts could not review the architect's decision (see e.g. PALANDT, note 1 to Section 317 BGB), if completing the contract on such matters were considered to be an act of "establishing" an obligation. But decisions on such matters are characterized differently there (see below, at FN 8).

[6] Clause 66 ICE Conditions; similarly Article 5.3 of the JCT Articles of Agreement

[7] E.g. with respect to adjustment of rates and prices in case of changes in quantities or of work not priced in the contract (Section 2 (3) and (6)); adjustment of a lump-sum price (Section 2(7)), extension of time on a variety of grounds (Section 6 (2)-(4)); determination of facts relevant for accounts and payments (Section 14 (2))

the rights and obligations of the contractor and the employer have to be clarified or adjusted. But, the employer and the contractor have to sort out themselves any differences, without assistance from a third person integrated into the structure of their contractual relationship. The parties have to reach agreement and if they don't, they have to go either to court or arbitration or to some other neutral institution unrelated to their contract and to the performance of the works. Such courts or other institutions decide the dispute by reference to what are considered to be objective criteria or by a supplementing interpretation of the contract. Their action normally is not considered to be the creation of an obligation[8] for which the parties may turn to a third party but not to a court.

Outside the scope of application of the VOB, one finds, however, contracts where the architect may make certain decisions comparable to those of the engineer or architect in England.[9]

An approach situated somewhere between the English system and the German VOB is that adopted in the French Public Works Contract Conditions (CCAG) and followed in a number of other countries which have adopted the French system. These conditions[10] distinguish on the employer's side between three entities : Le maître de l'ouvrage, i.e. the entity for which the works are performed and which can be described as the employer; la personne responsable du marché is the person officially designated to represent the employer in the performance of the contract[11]; the maître d'oeuvre is the person or the company, chosen for his technical qualification, who directs and controls the performance of the works; to describe this last named person, the term "supervisor of the works" has been used.[12] Apart from supervising the works, the maître d'oeuvre

---

[8] Such a creation of an obligation, under Section 317 of the BGB, can be assigned to a third person who may for instance determine equitably the price of a good or a service. Normally, such powers cannot be assigned to a court

[9] For examples, see WEICK p 225

[10] They are applicable both to building and to civil engineering works of the central Government, to local authorities and their establishments; see Circular of 21 January 1976 in JORF publication N° 2006

[11] "exécution du marché", as distinct from "exécution des travaux" for which the maître d'oeuvre is responsible

[12] MATHURIN, p 83

Apart from supervising the works, the maître d'oeuvre performs a number of functions similar to those of the engineer or architect in the English type of contract, but his decisions making powers are only a shadow of those in English contracts.

Thus, the maître d'oeuvre prepares, on the basis of a submission by the contractor, a monthly account.[13] This account forms the basis of the employer's payment obligation in a manner which, in some respects, resembles a payment certificate under an English type of contract but is devoid of any binding nature.[14] The maître d'oeuvre also proposes to the employer the acceptance of the works in a manner which is comparable to the completion certificate under an English type of contract.[15] He also has a number of other functions which may contribute to dispute avoidance or settlement but which differ in nature from those of an engineer in an English style contract.

As an illustration, one may mention the rules with respect to extension of time: the maître d'oeuvre has the power to grant such an extension in cases of exceptional weather conditions but only in two situations and in a strictly limited framework: where the work is suspended due to weather conditions as prescribed in legislative or regulatory provisions, the maître d'oeuvre extends the time for completion by the number of days during which the work was actually suspended on these grounds, but deducting the number of days for which the contractor should have made allowance. The second situation arises where the extension can be calculated by reference to criteria defined in the conditions of special application (CCAP).[16] In most other cases,[17] the extension is discussed between the contractor

---

[13] "Etat d'acompte", Article 13.21 and 13.22

[14] See Article 13.2 and Article 2.1 which lists under the function of the maître d'oeuvre "de proposer [le] règlement" of the works. Both the personne responsable du marché and the budgetary service of the Government must verify the monthly account and may make corrections (see VILLARD, et al. 262 seq)

[15] Article 41.1

[16] Article 19.22

[17] They are listed in Article 19.21 and include changes in quantities, certain variations, unforeseen site conditions, delay caused by the employer. For situations mentioned neither in Articles 19.22 nor in the list of 19.21, time extension requires an amendment to the contract (Article 19.23)

and the maître d'oeuvre; the latter makes a proposal to the person in charge of the performance of the contract. It is this person and not the maître d'oeuvre who takes the decision by which the contractor then has to abide until it might be reversed in the dispute settlement procedures which will be described presently.[18]

## 1.2 Early intervention of a neutral person (fact-finding by experts, provisional measures and pre-arbitral referee)

Where a contracting system does not provide for provisional dispute settlement as part of the contract management, the courts or other neutral bodies may have to intervene prior to a final settlement of the dispute in ordinary court or arbitration proceedings. The principal purposes of such interventions are the findings of fact, including those which may be necessary for the preservation of evidence, on the one hand and, on the other hand, directions or orders by which the parties in a provisional manner are required to adopt a certain conduct or perform certain acts prior to the final resolution of the dispute.

For fact-finding, a number of institutions and rules are available. In France, fact-finding by technical experts may be ordered by the civil courts, even before proceedings on the merits have been commenced.[19] In public work contracts, administrative tribunals[20] may order what is called a constat d'urgence.[21]

Similar procedures exist in Germany[22] and find their principal field of application in matters relating to construction contracts.[23] The proceedings which are conducted before party appointed experts requested to resolve disputes on technical issues,(i.e. disputes on facts, from the point of view the lawyers) are described as Schiedsgutachten and find their legal basis in sections 317-

---

[18] Articles 19.21, 2.52 and 50.11

[19] Articles 232 seq and 145 NCPC

[20] For their function see below section 1.5

[21] Article 104 CTA; see also AUBY and DRAGO sections 972-974

[22] Sections 485 - 494 ZPO

[23] KROPPEN/HEYERS/SCHMITZ p 23 note 21 INGENSTAU/KORBION Note 22 (a) at Section 18

319 of the Civil Code, the BGB.[24]

The VOB considers specifically disputes concerning materials and components, in particular their conformity with the contract. Either party may address itself to one of the many Materialprüfungssstellen,[25] i.e. offices established by the Government or authorized by it, with the request for a finding. Provided the other party has been informed of this request in time, the finding of the office is binding on the Parties.[26]

On the international level, the principal institution for organizing fact-finding and other investigations by technical experts is the International Centre for Technical Expertise established by the ICC in Paris. The Rules of this Centre provide for the appointment of experts, their terms of reference and the procedure to be followed by them.[27] In addition to any findings, he may be requested to make, the expert may be empowered to recommend measures appropriate for the performance of the contract or necessary in order to safeguard the subject matter; he may also supervise the carrying out of the contractual operations.[28] His findings or recommendations normally are not binding but the parties may agree to the contrary.[29]

The courts in most countries have powers to order provisional measures pending the final resolution of a dispute. As examples of well well developed procedural systems for such measures one may mention the einstweilige Verfügung under the German Code of Civil Procedure[30] and the

---

[24] See e.g. NICKLISCH/WEICK Notes 21 – 22 at Section 18; INGENSTAU/KORBION Note 17 at Section 18; SCHLOSSER Section 20–22 and comparison to similar institutions in other legal systems, Sections 23–28

[25] A directory to these offices has been published by the Verband der Materialprüfungsämter e.V. edited by CZECH "Wer prüft was?", Wiesbaden (Bauverlag).

[26] VOB/B Section 18 and INGENSTAU/KORBION Notes 13–19 at section 18

[27] ICC Brochure N° 307 and DERAINS; for a description of the ICC's experience with these rules see JARVIN

[28] Article 6.1 of the Rules

[29] Article 6.3

[30] Sections 935 – 945 ZPO

Ordonnance de référé in French civil[31] and administrative procedure.[32] Under such procedures, orders may be issued to the contractor concerning his work[33] and, by virtue of an order in référé provision, the employer may have to make interim payments.[34]

Some legal institutions which can be found in the practice of construction contracts combine elements of fact-finding and interim decisions of disputes. Thus, the collaudatore in Italy, as a neutral person settles disputes arising between the employer and the contractor during the performance of the works. He also intervenes in determining the quality of the work at the time of acceptance and is a cosignatory of the record of acceptance.[35]

Similarly, the French procedure of référé préventif is of particular importance in construction work: an expert is appointed to follow the progress of the work; he may intervene to prevent accidents or assist in the repair of damage. He submits a report if a dispute is brought to court.[36]

Powers to order provisional measures normally are vested in the courts. It has sometimes been argued that arbitrators do not have such powers and that in any event their decision in such matters are not enforceable as awards.[37] Some legislations expressly reserve such measures

---

[31] articles 484-492 NCPC regulates référé proceedings in which both sides are heard and Articles 493 – 498 proceedings sur requête in which orders are made ex parte.

[32] Articles R 102 and R 103 CTA, introduced 1955; for details, see AUBY and DRAGO Sections 962 – 971 (vol 2 pp 45 – 49)

[33] E.g. contractors have been ordered to return to the site their form work or to perform conservatory work (see AUBY and DRAGO Section 969)

[34] Article 809 (2) NCPC; for details see VINCENT and GUINCHARD: section 142 p 182 – 183. The payment ordered is provisional and not a final determination as in case of summary judgments under English law; for the difference see SCHLOSSER Section 414

[35] MATHURIN p 91

[36] VINCENT and GUINCHARD Section 143 p 184 and PEISSE

[37] For details. see SANDROCK/NÖCKER pp 75-82; KÜHN p 47 -51 and SCHLOSSER Sections 403-406 pp 303-309

to the courts.[38]

Where such express statutory restrictions do not apply, the parties may confer these powers on a arbitrator and it may well be argued that, where an interim decision rests on a substantive right, decisions of the arbitrator are enforceable as awards.[39] In any event, the parties to a contract may invest a third person with the power to make determinations of a permanent or interim nature affecting their contractual rights. An example of such "contractual" determination of rights is precisely the Engineer when he makes decisions affecting the Parties' rights and settles disputes in the course of their contract administration.

Thus, there should be no objection against a scheme by which a neutral person appointed by the Parties or an institution designated by them makes such orders for interim measures - the orders being contractually binding even if one denied them enforcement as arbitral awards.

The need for such a system was felt for instance in England. In fact, what I have described above as the English system of contract administration, while being generally adopted in prime contracts, rarely finds application in subcontracts. This gave rise to frequent disputes over payments when, in the absence of a certifying architect or engineer, the subcontractor believed that the prime contractor arbitrarily withheld payments due to him. As a remedy, one of the standard forms of sub-contract used in the building industry was amended to provide for the appointment of an "adjudicator" who may make simple and provisional decisions as to whether payment has to be made.[40] The system is said to have worked well. In practice relatively few adjudicators have had to be appointed, the introduction of the system, of itself, apparently imposed a certain discipline on main contractors.[41]

On the international level, a more ambitious system has been elaborated. After some ten years of preparatory

[38] E.g. Article 818 of the Italian Code Civil Procedure and Article 26 of the Swiss Uniform Law on Arbitration (The Concordat) for domestic arbitrations

[39] see in particular the demonstration by SCHLOSSER Sections 404 seq and 770 seq

[40] LLOYD: Arbitral Referee p 7

[41] ibid.

work,[42] the ICC has now created such a system which, as an anglicization of the _référé_ is called the <u>Pre-Arbitral Referee Procedure</u>.[43] Contrary to the expert in the ICC procedure described above, the referee has powers to make orders.

The Rules define the powers of the referee as follows:

"(a) To order any conservatory measures or any measures of restoration that are urgently necessary to prevent either immediate damage or irreparable loss and so to safeguard any of the rights or property of one of the parties.

(b) To order a party to make to any other party or to another person any payment which ought to be made.

(c) To order a party to take any step which ought to be taken according to the contract between the parties, including the signing or delivery of any document or the procuring by a party of the signature or delivery of a document.

(d) To order any measures necessary to preserve or establish evidence"[44]

The order of the Referee must be made within 30 days from the date on which the file was transmitted to him; but the time limit may be extended.[45] The order does not pre-judge the substance of the case but it remains in force unless and until the Referee or the jurisdiction competent for the merits of the case has decided otherwise.[46]

The Rules provide for international construction contracts the mechanism for provisionally resolving all those disputes which arise during the performance of the work and which would cause damage if their resolution would be delayed until an award by an arbitral tribunal.

---

[42] The work was introduced in 1980 by the note GOEDEL/SCHNEIDER; see also DERAINS pp 186 - 191

[43] PAULSSON

[44] Article 2.1

[45] Article 6.2

[46] Article 6.3

## 1.3    The preliminary reference

In England, the ICE Conditions provide that, before a dispute can be submitted to arbitration, it must be referred to the Engineer for his decision. If the Contractor is dissatisfied with this decision or if the Engineer does not render one within three months, the Contractor my bring the dispute to arbitration; otherwise he is bound by the Engineer's decision.[47]

Through the FIDIC Civil Conditions, the requirement of a preliminary reference to the Engineer found its way into many international contracts.

This requirement has been heavily criticized by a number of legal writers[48] while others found it useful.[49] As rightly pointed out by one of the leading specialists in English construction law and international practice: "It is sometimes forgotten how many disputes are and were resolved and continue to be resolved as a result of a thoughtful and considered decision of the engineer".[50] To reach such results, the practice traditionally followed by many consulting engineers, should be observed, referring the dispute to partners who had not been involved in the work in question, "so as to obtain a higher degree of independence and detachment from the dispute in question."[51] In any event, the prior reference to the Engineer is a binding requirement and effect has been given to the requirement of this preliminary reference in international arbitration. For instance in the ICC Award 4840, an arbitral tribunal held that it did not have jurisdiction over claims which had not previously been referred to the Engineer.[52]

The preliminary reference to the engineer is often considered to be a particularity of English contracting style and of the FIDIC Civil Conditions. In reality, however,

---

[47] Clause 66

[48] WALLACE p 169 and 1980 Supplement, BRABANT p 168

[49] SEPPALA p 323, HAUTOT/FLECHEUX p 620

[50] LLOYD in ILCR (1988) p 341

[51] ibid

[52] In 3 ICLR (1986/3) pp 277-284 with Comments JARVIN at p 282

it is neither of general use in England[53] nor unique to that country since similar requirements can be found in the rules and conditions elsewhere.

The German VOB, for instance, when it is applied in contracts with public authorities, recommends but does not require that the contractor address himself first to the authority immediately superior to that which is the contracting party on the employer's side. This superior authority affords the contractor an opportunity to argue his case and takes a decision which in principle should be made within two months. If the contractor, within a further period of two months, does not submit a written objection to the employer, the decision of the superior authority is taken as being accepted, provided the contractor has been warned of this consequence.[54]

The French Public Works Conditions go even further than the ICE and FIDIC Civil Conditions and provide for a mandatory preliminary reference in two stages.[55] Any difference between the contractor and the maître d'oeuvre must first be transmitted to the maître d'oeuvre with a reasoned statement indicating the amounts claimed. He forwards the contractor's statement to the person responsible for the contract and attaches a statement of his own position. The person responsible for the contract, within a period of two months, makes a proposal for the settlement of the dispute; failing such a proposal the request is considered to be rejected.

If the contractor is not satisfied with the proposal or the rejection, he must, within a further period of three months, make known to the person responsible for the contract his objections and file an additional statement developing his reasons for refusal. He must do likewise if the original dispute arose not with the maître d'oeuvre but with the person responsible for the contract. This statement is transmitted to the employer who must decide within three months, failing which the contractor may submit the dispute to the competent administrative tribunal. If a decision has been made by the employer, the contractor has six months to attack it before the administrative tribunal; if he fails to do so, the decision becomes final. In any event, the modalities set out in the employer's decision apply until modified by the administrative tribunal.

---

[53] Building contracts, and in particular the most frequently used JCT standard forms do not require such preliminary reference.

[54] VOB/B Section 18 (2)

[55] Articles 50 CCAG

### 1.4 Conciliation and other non contentious dispute settlement procedures

In France, Belgium and some other countries, special conciliation mechanisms are provided and applicable to Government contracts. In <u>France</u>, a <u>consultative committee for amicable settlement</u> has been set up in the Office of the Prime Minister.[56] Its function is to seek, in disputes relating to Government contracts, legal and factual elements which may be adopted in fairness to bring about an amicable solution. The Committee may be seized by public authorities at any time. A contractor may seize it once the contract has been performed and his claims have been rejected by the person responsible for the contract. The Committee must give its opinion within six months. The public authority then has two months to notify to the contractor its own decision which may not follow the recommendations of the Committee. If it fails to do so in this period, the contractor's claim is rejected.

A similar institution exists in <u>Belgium</u>, i.e. the <u>Comité supérieur de contrôle</u> to which both public authorities and contractors may addressed themselves for an advisory opinion on the dispute. If the public administration does not follow the opinion of the <u>Comité</u>, it must state in writing its reasons for not doing so.[57]

This committee now also may conduct conciliation proceedings and make settlement proposals. If these proceedings do not succeed to bring about a settlement, the parties may follow the procedure for an advisory opinion by the committee.

Different types of non contentious procedures exist in <u>Germany</u> before the VOB Advisory Offices.[58] Such offices have been set up in several of the <u>Länder</u>. They may be called to give advice or recommendations but may not make binding decisions.[59]

Furthermore, there have been attempts in Germany to promote settlement of construction disputes by specified conciliation offices, the <u>Bau-Schlichtungsstellen</u>.[60]

---

[56] Comité consultatif de règlement amiable, Articles 239-246 of the <u>Code des marchés publics</u>

[57] For details see FLAMME/MATHEY/FLAMME pp 751 - 760

[58] <u>VOB Prüf- und Beratungsstellen</u>

[59] WEICK, p 225

[60] INGENSTAU/KORBION, p 1760

## 1.5    Court proceedings

Disputes under construction contracts, whether they arise under contracts between private parties or with public authorities, in most European countries are subject to the jurisdiction of the ordinary courts.

In some jurisdictions, special rules for construction litigation have been developed and specialized branches of the courts may be set up to deal with such cases. A particularly successful example can be found in England where the "Official Referees' Courts" have become the specialized jurisdiction for construction disputes.[61]

In France, public works contracts, by statutory provision, are characterized as administrative contracts.[62] As a consequence, any public works contract in France is an administrative contract, irrespective of the nature of its provisions; a public authority may not choose, as it may do in the case of other transactions, such as the supply of goods or transport services, to make public works under the common law of contract. As a result, disputes under such public works contracts are subject to a special jurisdiction, the administrative tribunals with, at a top of the hierarchy, the Conseil d'Etat.

## 1.6    Arbitration

In most countries of the European Community, arbitration is available for disputes both under public and private construction contracts and in many of them, arbitration is frequently used.

In England, the principal sets of contract conditions for public and private contracts provide for dispute settlement in arbitration. Arbitration clauses are contained in the public works conditions of the central Government,[63] in the JCT Standard Forms for Building Contracts both in

---

[61] See FAY in ICLR (1984) p 357 and his book on Official Referees' Business

[62] Article 4 of an enactment made during the French revolution which still today is quoted, by reference to the calendar then used, as the Act of 28 Pluviose of the year VIII. For the text of the provision see De LAUBADERE/MODERNE/DELVOVE: Contracts administratifs vol 1 N° 202; see ibid N° 93; and DUFAU p 97

[63] Condition 61 of the General Conditions of Government Contracts for Building and Civil Engineering Works ( GC/Works 1, 2nd ed 1977)

their versions for local authorities and for private clients[64] and in the ICE Civil Engineering Conditions.[65]

The arbitration clause in the JCT forms, as one of its interesting features, provides a possibility of joining proceedings under several contracts. The Royal Institute of Architects (RIBA) provides guidance for arbitration under the JCT forms[66] but has not issued any arbitration rules as the ICE has done. The earlier version of those ICE Rules, like most other construction arbitration rules,[67] showed little effort to provide for the particularities of construction arbitration; the guidance notes for its application even advised the arbitrator to follow the rules of procedure before the High Court.[68]

In 1983, the ICE procedure was fundamentally revised in a probably unique attempt to respond by arbitration rules to the particular problem arising in construction disputes in a manner which differs considerably from English rules and practices in arbitration and court procedures.[69] Among its special features one may mention the emphasis on a proper organization of the proceedings and a preparation of the hearing by written pleadings and procedural meetings so that the hearing itself is concentrated on the essential aspects of the case. The Rules also provide for a Short Procedure for Experts, Interim Arbitration, Protective Measures and Summary Awards. As one of the noteworthy features of ICE arbitration, one should also mention the List of Arbitrators with useful details on qualifications, experience and fields of interest of the persons considered by the Institution to be competent arbitrators.[70]

The practice of arbitration in England is wide spread in disputes with local authorities and between private parties. Disputes, under contracts with the central Government, however, very rarely go to arbitration, and

[64] Article 5 of the Articles of Agreement in all versions, 1980 edition

[65] Clause 66

[66] The Architect as Arbitrator

[67] For a comparison of a number of such rules see SCHNEIDER: Schiedsverfahren p 162 - 173

[68] The ICE Arbitration Procedure (1973) p 22

[69] Detailed commentary by HAWKER/UFF/TIMMS; see also SCHNEIDER in Bulletin ASA 1984

[70] HAWKER/UFF/TIMMS p 53; SCHNEIDER op.cit p 168

court proceedings in this field are almost unknown.[71]

In <u>Germany</u>, the construction industry has established arbitration rules[72] which are frequently used in private contracts.[73] For Government contracts, the VOB/A envisages the possibility of recourse to arbitration;[74] but in domestic Government contracts, arbitration does not seem to be used frequently. In international contracts, however, the Government is more readily inclined to accept arbitration. The Ministry of Defense has a standard arbitration agreement providing for ICC arbitration.[75]

It is important to point out that, under German law, an agreement to arbitrate may not be contained in the contract itself but must be made in a separate document.[76] This restriction does not apply where the contract is a commercial transaction for both parties; it does however apply to Government contracts.[77]

Concerning other countries of the Community, it is reported that arbitration is frequently used in <u>Italy</u>.[78] In <u>Denmark</u>, the General Conditions for Works and Supplies for Building and Civil Engineering Works[79], refer all disputes to the Court of Arbitration for Building and Civil

---

[71] BLYTH p 69

[72] <u>Schiedsgerichtsordnung für das Bauwesen</u> issued by the Deutscher Betonverein e.V. and the Deutsche Gesellschaft für Baurecht e.V. First edition in 1909, latest edition 1978, see WIEGAND pp 107 and 108.

[73] WIEGAND explains that "[t]oday, the bulk of construction disputes, particularly in the field of civil engineering contracts, is settled or decided" under these Rules (p 106 seq); see also HEIERMANN in <u>Jahrbuch</u> p 23. On the arbitration procedure, see HEIERMANN/KROPPEN: <u>Kommentar</u> and SCHNEIDER: Schiedsverfahren pp 171-172

[74] VOB/A Section 10(5) points out that an arbitration agreement must be made in a separate document (see below at FN 75).

[75] See ZDZIEBLO in DAUB/MEIERROSE/EBERSTEIN: <u>VOL Kommentar</u> p 291; for the text see DAUB/EBERSTEIN: <u>VOL</u> p 147

[76] Section 1027, ZPO

[77] See e.g. INGENSTAU/KORBION p 324 Section 40

[78] MATHURIN: <u>Provisional Text</u>, p 368

[79] <u>Almindelige Betingelser</u> (AB)

Engineering Works in Copenhagen. This court is administrated by the same Danish Institute of Arbitration which also administers the Copenhagen Court of International Arbitration.[80]

The most successful construction arbitration scheme is probably the Arbitration Council in the Netherlands.[81] This council has been formed some eighty years ago and is used for the settlement of construction disputes both under Government and private contracts.[82] The Council is formed of some one hundred members appointed in equal proportions by the Royal Institute of Engineers, the professional organization of architects and the federation of the contractors. Some twenty extraordinary members, most of whom are lawyers, are appointed by the Council itself. All appointments must be approved by the Minister of Transport and Waterways, the principal employer for public works contracts in the Netherlands.

The arbitrators are chosen by the parties from among the members of the Council and may be assisted by legal assessors. The Council provides also for an accelerated procedure where the hearing does not last for more than a day. Even ordinary procedures, often are settled in less than a year; only a quarter of the cases lasts for more than 18 months. Average costs are said to be of 3'600 Dutch Guilders, i.e. of some £ 1'100.[83]

With respect to France, it has been explained that private contracts frequently contain a clause where disputes are decided finally by the architect. However, because of the close links between the architect and the employer, such clauses have been held to be null and void.[84]

Disputes under public works contracts, as previously explained, in principle are subject to the jurisdiction of the administrative tribunals. Arbitration my be agreed only

---

[80] HALD p 187

[81] Raad van Arbitrage voor de Bouwbedrijven in Nederland

[82] See Vijfenzeventig Jaar; GOUDSMIT; SCHNEIDER: Schiedsverfahren pp 170 - 171 and MATHURIN Provisional Text p 424; there is also the Raad van Arbitrage voor Metaalnijverheid en Handel (Arbitration Council for the Metal Industry and Trade) which is used occasionally for the settlement of construction disputes.

[83] MATHURIN: Provisional Text p 425; he considers costs in this order to be a disadvantage.

[84] LIET-VEAUX, p 272

exceptionally for the settlement of accounts. An agreement to this effect may be made only after the dispute has arisen and must be specially approved. The case law which admits arbitration clauses by the Government and other public entities in international contracts does not apply to those contracts which are necessarily subject to the jurisdiction of the administrative tribunals. Contrary to what is occasionally affirmed, arbitration clauses in French public works contracts are invalid, even if the contract is international.[85]

For arbitration under civil engineering contracts, the Fédération nationale des travaux publics (FNTP) has prepared arbitration rules. Because of the restrictions just described concerning arbitration of disputes under public works contracts, these rules are applied primarily in disputes under sub-contracts.[86]

The specialized construction arbitration institutions just described deal primarily with domestic contracts and disputes. They rarely seem to be concerned with international cases.

International construction disputes in Europe concern primarily overseas projects. Since many overseas Governments, if they accept to submit disputes under public works contracts to arbitration, require that the arbitration be held in their country, construction arbitration in Europe predominantly, but not exclusively, concerns disputes under sub-contracts or joint-ventures for overseas projects.

Such international disputes often raise difficult legal questions of a kind which does not arise in domestic disputes, such as issues as conflict of laws, foreign and comparative law, foreign and international standards and practices. Frequently the projects to which these disputes relate are of a size far greater than the ordinary disputes in domestic arbitration; as a result of the high financial interests at stake, greater amounts of money are spent on legal, technical and commercial advisors, and the procedure becomes more complex. Furthermore, the international nature of the dispute and the different origin of the parties, of their counsel and of the arbitrators often require great efforts and skill in intercultural communications.

Under these circumstances, it is not surprising that, beside the specialized domestic construction arbitration

---

[85] AUBY and DRAGO p 50 (Section 23) and 51 (Section 25); DUFAU pp 187 seq.

[86] For further details see VILLARD with the text of the Rules pp 51–55 and SCHNEIDER: Schiedsverfahren pp 172–173

systems, institutions and systems have developed which deal essentially with international arbitration in a variety of substance matters, including construction. While many arbitrations take place in an institutional framework, others are conducted on an <u>ad hoc</u> basis. One can hardly know the number of <u>ad hoc</u> construction arbitrations proceeding according to the Arbitration Rules of UNCITRAL or the ECE, or simply under the local arbitration legislation; but judging from the present writer's experience, it is likely to be relatively high.

A number of organizations and institutions in many countries of Europe play a role in international arbitration, in setting the institutional framework, acting as appointing authority or providing other assistance to the proceedings. Perhaps the most frequently used centres of this arbitration activity are those in London, Paris and Switzerland. In addition, mention must be made of those of the Netherlands, Belgium, Germany, Italy, Spain and, primarily with respect to East-West transactions, Vienna and Stockholm, as fora for international construction arbitration.

The most important institution for international construction disputes is undoubtedly the <u>ICC Court of International Arbitration</u>.[87] At the end of 1989, there were some 700 cases pending, of which 309 had been filed during that year. During the last four years, the share of ICC cases in the field of construction varied between 18.5 and 26.4% of the total case load. A large share of the cases, varying from year to year between 40 and 50%, is for amounts in dispute above 1 million US$. In 1989 the disputed amount in 12.7% of the pending cases exceeded 10 million US$.[88]

The ICC arbitration system and its Rules, of which the latest edition is in force as from 1st January 1988[89], have been criticized at times. But they have the great advantage of being well established in the industry and resting on many years of experience. The rules allow much flexibility and may be accommodated to respond to arbitration traditions from different legal systems and to the needs of various kinds of disputes.

The ICC Commission on International Arbitration considered whether action was required to adapt the Rules specifically for the needs of construction arbitration.

---

[87] For a well documented and reasoned description of the ICC Arbitration see CRAIG/PARK/PAULSSON

[88] ICC Annual Report 1989 p 21

[89] ICC Publication N° 447

Apart from the creation of the Pre-arbitral Referee Procedure mentioned above, no such adaptation was considered to be necessary.

## 2. SOME RECENT ARRANGEMENTS FOR DISPUTE SETTLEMENT IN LARGE PROJECTS

Outside Europe, there have been a number of instances where, beyond a more or less standard arbitration clause, mechanisms and rules were established to provide efficient settlement of disputes.

2.1 An example which gained some celebrity is the Claims Review Board as applied in the El Cajon Project in Honduras.[90] At the proposal of A.A. Matthews, advisor to the employer, the Honduras National Electricity Board (E.N.E.E.), the parties decided to establish a Claims Review Board as a permanent institution to function throughout the contract period.

The Board was composed of three members, one having been appointed and paid by each of the parties and a third jointly by the parties. Its members visited the site at least three times a year to keep abreast of construction activities and problems. Whenever disputes arose, either the contractor or the employer could refer them to the Board which, after having heard the parties gave its decision. This decision could be attacked in ICC arbitration within sixty days. It is reported that all disputes which arose during the project were satisfactorily settled by the Board. None had to be brought to arbitration.

2.2 Another system of interest is that developed for the construction of the Metropolitan Atlanta Rapid Transit Authority (MARTA) in Atlanta, Georgia.[91] Its interest, for our subject, lies primarily in the fact that contract documents and dispute settlement mechanisms for all contracts related to this large project were standardized. In view of the differences existing in the United States between Federal, State and local contracting laws and procedures, this standardization is comparable to that which may be required in international projects.

The system provided for several instances of prior

---

[90] Description based on LODIGIANI and information provided to the author by Dr. Ing. Igor Valerio LETO, one of the Board's members

[91] GOLEMBIEWSKI et al.

internal review of claims by the engineer and the employer's organization, each involving, on the employer's side, a higher level of responsibility. The final stage was arbitration under the Construction Industry Arbitration Rules of the American Arbitration Association.

All contractors of the employer undertook to include corresponding clauses in their sub-contracts for work and supplies so that the same procedures also applied to sub-contractors and proceedings could be merged.

2.3    In the construction of the Vancouver Advanced Light Rapid Transit System (ALRT), it was provided that disputes arising during the course of the construction were settled by a referee.[92] The system relied on a proposal which Sir Edward Singleton had made at the time in the International Bar Association and to the ICC.[93]

As soon as the contract was concluded, and without waiting for a dispute to arise, the parties jointly appointed the referee whose mandate lasted until the end of the contract, including the reliability demonstration in the second year of operation. They choose a professional engineer who had just taken early retirement from the Canadian Federal Civil Service. The contract provided that the parties could turn to him at any time for immediate interim resolution of all disputes relating to the interpretation of the contract and to the parties' rights thereunder.

It was specified that the referee had to act in "as an expert and not as an arbitrator". The referee was required to afford to both parties an opportunity to present their position but was not bound by strict rules of evidence nor by rules of court and arbitration procedure. His decisions were binding upon the parties until completion of the work. Thereafter, they could be challenged in the competent jurisdiction, i.e. the courts of the Province of British Columbia.

The project run into great difficulties which partly were attributed to the haste with which the contract had been drawn up and awarded in order to meet the deadline for completion, i.e. the 1986 World Fair in Vancouver. Persons involved with the project believed that it was only thanks to the role of the referee and the competence with which he handled the numerous and complex disputes that a reasonable

---

[92] Information provided to the author by H.D.C. HUNTER, Esq.

[93] See bibliography: SINGLETON

settlement without protracted court proceedings could be found.

2.4    In Europe, such schemes seem to be rare, if not unknown. Normally arbitration clauses are provided which show little consideration of the particular problems and needs of construction projects.

2.5    With respect to the project for the Eurotunnel, the Channel Fixed Link, there are two basic instruments: (a) the Treaty between the U.K. and the French Republic and (b) the Concession Agreement between the two Governments and the two groups of contractors appointed as Concessionaires. Both instruments provide for arbitration under the Treaty.

Since this enormous project was based on a treaty between the two Governments concerned which regulated many aspects of the construction and operation of the tunnel, one might have thought that the parties would have seized the opportunity to establish a uniform dispute settlement mechanism, suitable for the project.

Compared to this expectation, the arbitration mechanism established under Article 15 of the Treaty is somewhat disappointing. It applies only to disputes concerning the Treaty between the two States and to disputes between the States and the Concessionaires. The clause makes reference neither to the disputes under the construction contract nor to those under the various other contracts for supply and work which had to be concluded for the implementation of the project.

The mechanism provided by the Treaty is rather heavy, since disputes which are not limited to the two States have to be brought before arbitral tribunals of five members. Proceedings before such tribunals are likely to be rather cumbersome.

The various contracts for work and supply contain arbitration clauses separate from each other. The principal construction contract is based on the FIDIC Civil Conditions. In its Clause 67, it provides for the preliminary reference to the Maître d'oeuvre corresponding to the reference to the Engineer in the ICE and the FIDIC Civil Conditions. If the decision of the Maître d'oeuvre fails to settle the dispute, it may be submitted to ICC arbitration in Brussels.

2.6    One of the other large European projects with an important international dimension is the construction of the Large Electron Positron Storage Ring (LEP) which the European Organization for Nuclear Research (CERN) constructed in the underground of the Geneva region and the neighbouring part of France. The construction contracts provide for the application of three different sets of contract conditions, those of the CERN, the General Conditions of the Swiss Association of Engineer and Architects (SIA Standard 118) and the third edition of the FIDIC Civil Conditions. With respect to disputes, the provision contained in the CERN Conditions applied, setting out an <u>ad hoc</u> procedure with a reference to the law of procedure in the canton of Zurich, to be applied by analogy.

2.7    While these and other dispute settlement clauses in major international projects in Europe show little preoccupation with particular problems in construction disputes, the discussions about innovative approaches is beginning to bear fruit. Some major construction projects are now being negotiated or implemented in Europe which provide for some simplified procedures prior to arbitration. In one such contract, disputes are first referred to on technical or financial panel, acting as independent experts and not as arbitrators. A unanimous decision of the Panel is final and binding. Other decisions may be attacked first in a procedure resembling that of an American style Mini-Trial and then in arbitration.

However, contracts providing such dispute settlement mechanisms other than arbitration still seem to be the exception.

3.    PROPOSALS FOR EUROPEAN HARMONIZATION OR COORDINATION

In the context of the work preparing for the European single market, proposals have been made for harmonization if not standardization of many aspects of construction laws and regulations. An important contribution to this work is Claude MATHURIN's study on <u>Responsibilities, Duties and Insurance in the Construction Industry</u> with a view to harmonization at Community level, the Final Report of this study having been published by the Commission on 2 February 1990.[94]

As    part    of    a    "Community    wide    system    of responsibility, guarantees and insurance in construction", Mr. MATHURIN proposes the definition and institution of a "<u>permanent Community conciliation and arbitration system</u>".[95] This part of his proposal met with a favorable reaction from the various groups consulted by him. In particular, a great

---

[94] See Bibliography

[95] Final Report pp 11, 22–23, 27, 32–33, 91–92

majority of the design professionals, the "clients" and public administration included the proposal in their priority areas.[96]

Although the proposal does not provide much detail with respect to its structure and implementation, it appears desirable for a conference such as this to give some thought to what can and should be done in the field.

Harmonization of procedural matters as those concerning the settlement of construction disputes has, of course, its ramifications both in the substantive law of construction and in the law of civil procedure and arbitration. Action in the field of dispute settlement, therefore, must be seen in the context of the present state of the law on these substance matters in the Member States and in that of programmes for their harmonization.

The following considerations are of a more modest scope. They aim primarily at presenting some more immediate measures which may be taken to improve the flow of construction activities within the single market by reducing the transactional costs caused by disputes between parties from different member countries and by facilitating their settlement.

## 3.1 Inventory of existing procedures and institutions and their adaptation to work in a European context

The explanations in the preceding sections of this paper have given an indication of the great number and variety of procedures and institutions which exist already in Europe. Thus, it appears that most of the constituent elements for a performing European system for the settlement of construction disputes have been developed already. What is needed is (a) to make an inventory of these institutions and procedures (b) make their existence known beyond their present field of application, (c) adapt the purely domestic ones to an operation in the European context and (d) ensure that the international ones respond to the needs of the European single market.

3.1.1 A first important step would consist in establishing a directory, data base or both of institutions providing advice and expertise on technical matters in the settlement of disputes. The information collected should include areas of technical expertise and procedures of each institution. It should also state the linguistic capabilities of the institution and inform whether it is in a position to respond to requests by persons or enterprises from other Member

---

[96] Final Report, pp 35, 39

countries, working in the geographical area which the institution serves or to request for services in other countries.

3.1.2 It must be expected that at present the work of most of these institutions relates only to domestic contracts. Efforts should be made to make them responsive to work in a European context. The enquiry just described may be a first step in this direction.

3.1.3 The need to develop responsiveness to the European dimension also applies to many specialized domestic arbitration institutions. The procedures developed and the specific experience accumulated provide them with an important potential, especially for smaller disputes. It should be suggested to them to examine how they can adapt their structures and procedures so that parties from other Member countries (e.g. a contractor performing work in the country of the institution), may have full confidence in the institution.

One might think of enlarging the list of arbitrators to include persons familiar with different contracting methods and legal systems and conversant in foreign languages. Another approach might consist in establishing links with foreign construction arbitration institutions or with bodies familiar with the particularities of the international dimension in disputes.

3.1.4 Action along these lines hopefully will contribute to adapt existing institutions to the needs of a European construction market. Beyond this effect, it may also open the institutions described to the European market. This may then contribute to the development of a single market in the services related to the settlement of construction disputes, services which are now provided only on the national markets.

3.2    European system for urgent decisions during the performance of the work

In addition to the adaptation of existing domestic procedures and institutions to the European dimension, one might also consider the possibility of developing certain procedures and institutions for use throughout Europe.

3.2.1 Efforts in this direction should give particular attention to mechanisms for rapid decisions during the construction process. Some such decisions, for instance those on the quality and conformity of materials and components, may and perhaps should be final. If they are final, they must be rendered by persons or institutions of unquestioned qualification and impartiality. The Community or the Member Governments may have a role to play in providing the necessary assurances.

3.2.2 Most issues which arise during the performance of the works, however, should not be decided in a final manner. This includes also those issues related to materials and components where, as it is often the case, the quality and conformity is not a straight-forward technical or testing question but calls for the interpretation of the contract documents, regulations and standards.

3.2.3 In these and many other aspects, urgent decisions are called for so that the works can proceed. Since the decision is made under the pressure of time, there is an increased risk that the parties have not fully analyzed all relevant aspects and that the deciding person, competent and impartial as he may be, makes a "wrong" decision. A review of the decision in proper proceedings therefore must be reserved.

However, if the urgent decisions are made by competent and impartial persons or, if those made by one party or its agents are subject to immediate control by such persons, the need for final reviews in ordinary proceedings is likely to be much reduced. The approximation thus reached in the provisional decisions in many cases is likely to be satisfactory to the parties. In most cases, the provisional decision can be expected to be sufficiently close to what the parties may consider the "right" or an "acceptable" decision so that they will not be inclined to spend time and money in court or arbitration proceedings with uncertain outcome.

3.2.4 The English system of contract management by an architect or engineer appears as a very suitable solution which deserves to be considered for more general application. However, corrections would seem to be required in two areas:

(a) It has often been pointed out that, in the course of his contract administration, the engineer or architect may have to make decisions which can affect his own liability to the employer; in such cases, an immediate review of the decision should be available.

(b) As a central element of the system, certification assures the contractor of regular progress payments, reflecting the work actually performed. Complaints have been voiced that, especially where the certifying engineer or architect is on the employer's payroll, insufficient amounts are certified. The amount certified or the refusal to certify any amount, therefore, should be subject to immediate review by an "adjudicator" or, as proposed by the present author, a "review certifier".[97]

3.2.5 The English system, as described above, normally is not applicable in sub-contracts. Because of habits formed by different contracting methods, it might be difficult to adopt it in countries with different traditions.[98] In these countries, private and public employers may not be prepared to confer on an engineer, architect or maître d'oeuvre powers as wide as those of an engineer under the ICE Conditions or an architect under the JCT Contract Forms. But they should accept that those of their decisions which are of serious consequence for the contractor, are subject to immediate review by a neutral person.

3.2.6 In those countries where systems for intervention by a neutral person exist, as for instance the collaudatore in Italy, the necessary arrangements should be made to adapt the mechanism to contracts with foreign parties.

3.2.7 In other countries, it is recommended to use, with the necessary adaptations, the system of the Pre-Arbitral Referee Procedure developed by the ICC. The ten years of preparatory work in the ICC have shown that the elaboration of such an internationally acceptable mechanism is a difficult and time consuming enterprise. For the European Community to spend time and funds on the development of a different system would be justified only if it were shown that the Pre-Arbitral Referee Procedure is not suitable for the desired purpose. Since this procedure was developed precisely for situations as those described above and since its preparation associated representatives from the industry and specialists in construction and international arbitration, there is no reason to doubt that it will prove to be a suitable instrument.

However, for the specific purposes considered here it appears desirable that, especially with respect to the choice of a competent Pre-Arbitral Referee and for wider acceptance of the system, arrangements be made for cooperation with existing domestic institutions having experience in the settlement of construction disputes.

3.2.8 Through such a system of rapid but provisional decision by a competent impartial person, accessible

---

[97] SCHNEIDER: Schiedsverfahren pp 234-236 and in ICLR (1984) pp 319-321

[98] Those who are familiar with international construction projects will know the difficulties which engineering firms from countries not using the English system face when they have to act as the engineer for instance under a FIDIC Civil type of contract.

anywhere in Europe, contractors in one European country will be assured of a fair treatment in other countries of the Community. Especially for small and middle sized contractors, this assurance may be of crucial importance when deciding whether they should face the risks and difficulties working abroad in the framework of unfamiliar contracting systems and practices. Thus, the system may make a useful contribution to increasing the flow of construction work in the single market.

BIBLIOGRAPHICAL REFERENCES

The Architect as Arbitrator, London (Royal Institute of Architects) revised edition 1978, 72 p

AUBY, Jean-Marie and DRAGO, Roland: Traité de contentieux administratif, Paris (LGDJ) 3rd ed 1984, 2 vols 1014 and 718 p

BLYTH, Alfred: United Kingdom, Government Contracts: Resolution of Disputes. Paper presented to the American Bar Association Conference on Disputes Resolution in International Public Contracting (July 1985) pp 45-74

BRABANT, André: Le contrat international de construction, Brussels (Bruylant) 1981 479 p

BRECHON, Christine: La Réforme des Comités consultatifs de règlements amiables, Actualité Juridique, Droit Administratif (1981) pp 304 seq

CRAIG, W. Lawrence; PARK, William W. and PAULSSON Jan: International Chamber of Commerce Arbitration, New York (Oceana) 2nd ed 1990

DAUB, Walter/EBERSTEIN, Hans Herrmann (Ed.): VOL, Verdingungsordnung für Leistungen (ausgenommen Bauleistungen), Düsseldorf (Werner Verlag) 23rd ed, 1984, 700 p

DAUB, Walter; MEIERROSE, Rudolf; EBERSTEIN, Hans Hermann: Kommentar zur VOL/A, Düsseldorf (Werner Verlag) 3rd ed 1985, 656 p

DERAINS, Yves: Technical Expertise and "référé arbitral", Report to the 1982 Hamburg ICCA Congress, in ICCA Congress Series N° 1 Deventer (Kluwer) 1983 pp 183-191; French version in Revue de l'arbitrage 1982 pp 239-251

DUFAU, Jean: Le droit des travaux publics, Paris (Moniteur) 1984, 335 p

FAY, Edgar: Official Referees' Business, London (Sweet & Maxwell) 2nd ed 1988, 270 p

FAY, Edgar: The Resolution of Construction Disputes in England and Wales 1 ICLR (1984/4) pp 357-370

FLAMME, Maurice-André; MATHEI, Philippe and FLAMME, Philippe: Commentaire pratique de la réglementation des marchés publics, Brussels (Confédération nationale de la construction) 5th ed 1986, 1226 p

GOLEMBIEWSKI, Robert T. TRATINER, Jeffrey B and MILLER, Gerald J.: Designing an Arbitration System for a Mass Transportation Construction Project, reprinted from The Arbitration Journal (1979) in Construction Arbitration: Selected Readings, New York (American Arbitration Association), 1981  pp 79-102

GOEDEL, Joachim and SCHNEIDER, Michael E.: Note to Introduce the Discussion on Arbitration of Construction Disputes at the International Arbitration Commission of the ICC on 16 October 1980, ICC Document N° 420/INT.110

GOUDSMIT, J.J.: Arbitration in Construction Contracts in International Financial Law Review June 1982 pp 28-33

HALD, Ole: The Danish General Conditions for Civil Works and Supplies for Building and Civil Engineering Works 1 ICLR (1984) pp 186-188

HAUTOT, Isabelle and FLECHEUX, Georges: La Clause de règlement des différends dans les Conditions F.I.D.I.C. génie civil de 1987, Revue de l'Arbitrage (1989/4) pp 609-629

HEIERMANN, Wolfgang: Die Schiedsgerichtsvereinbarung im nationalen und internationalen Bauvertrag 1 Jahrbuch (1987) pp 23-33

HEIERMANN, Wolfgang and KROPPEN, Heinz: Kommentar zur Schiedsgerichtsordnung für das Bauwesen, Wiesbaden (Bauverlag) 1975, 80 p

HAWKER, Geoffrey; UFF, John and TIMMS, Charles: The Institution of Civil Engineers' Arbitration Practice, London (Telford) 1986 244 p

INGENSTAU, Heinz and KORBION Hermann: VOB, Verdingungs- ordnung für Bauleistungen, Teile A und B, Kommentar, Düsseldorf (Werner Verlag) 10th ed, 1984, 1849 p

The Institution of Civil Engineers' Arbitration Procedure
(1983) with Introduction, Notes for Guidance and Annexes,
London (ICE) 1976, 44 p

JARVIN, Sigward: Die Erfahrungen der ICC mit technischen
Gutachten (with summary in English) in : NICKLISCH (ed): Der
komplexe Langzeitvertrag, Heidelberg (Müller) 1987 pp 551-567

KROPPEN, Heinz M.; HEYERS, Karl and SCHMITZ, Peter:
Beweissicherung im Bauwesen, Wiesbaden/Berlin (Bauverlag)
1982, 356 p

de LAUBADERE, André; MODERNE, Franck and DELVOVE, Pierre:
Traité des Contrats Administratifs, Paris (LGDJ) 2 ed; vol 1
(1983), 808 p vol 2 (1984) 1124 p

LIET-VEAUX, Georges: Le Droit de la construction, Paris
(Librairie technique) 8th ed 1984

LODIGIANI, G.: A "Claims Review Board" As a Way for an
Amicable Settlement of Disputes, and Other Considerations on
the Subject of Claims 3 ICLR (1986) pp 498-503

LLYOD, Humphrey: The Arbitral Referee - A proposal Deserving
Serious Consideration. Contribution to the Bordeaux Congress
of the Association internationale des jeunes avocats 1984, 14p

LLYOD, Humphrey: An Expanded Power to Decide? Effect of Two
Cases on the Engineer's Power under Clause 67 of the F.I.D.I.C.
Conditions 5 ICLR (1988) pp 326-341

MATHURIN, Claude: Study of Responsibilities, Guarantees and
Insurance in the Construction Industry with a view to
Harmonization at Community Level Final Report (condensed
version), Brussels 2 February 1990, (ECC, Reference
III/8326/89 - EN), 113 p

MATHURIN, Claude: Controls, Contracts, Liability and
Insurance in the Construction Industry in the European
Community provisional text, Brussels 12 february 1990 (EEC
Reference: III/3908/ 88 - EN), 516 p (quoted: MATHURIN :
Provisional Text

NICKLISCH, Fritz and WEICK, Günter: VOB, Verdingungsordnung für Bauleistungen, Teil B, Munich (Beck) 1981, 695 p

PAULSSON, Jan: A Better Mousetrap: 1990 ICC Rules for a Pre-
Arbitral Referee Procedure 18 International Business Lawyer
(May 1990) pp 214-219

PEISSE: Le "référé préventif" en matière de construction
immobilière, La Gazette du Palais 1975, 2.D. 426

KÜHN, Wolfgang: Vorläufiger Rechtsschutz und
Schiedsgerichtsbarkeit 1 Jahrbuch (1987) pp 47-62

SANDROCK, Otto and NÖCKER, Thomas: Einstweilige Massnahmen
internationaler Schiedsgerichte: blosse Papiertieger? 1
Jahrbuch (1987) pp 74-93

SCHLOSSER, Peter: Das Recht der internationalen privaten
Schiedsgerichtbarkeit, Tübingen (Mohr) 2nd ed 1989 791 p

SCHNEIDER, Michael E.; Die neue Bauschiedsgerichts-
verfahrensordnung der Institution of Civil Engineers, London
Bulletin de l'Association suisse de l'Arbitrage(1984) pp 39-45

SCHNEIDER, Michael E.: International Construction Contracts,
in: Droit et Pratique du Commerce International 1983 vol 9 N°
pp 277-322 N° 3 pp 430-477 and N° 4 pp 649-686

SCHNEIDER, Michael E.: Schiedsverfahren in Streitigkeiten aus
Bau- und Anlagenverträgen/Arbitration of Construction
Disputes, in Contracts and Dispute Settlement in Civil
Engineering and Construction of Plants, Schriftenreihe des
Deutschen Instituts für Schiedsgerichtswesen/German
Institute of Arbitration, vol. 4, Cologne etc. (Heymanns)
(1981), pp 159-186 and 187-244; the conclusions and the
proposal for a "review certifier" reproduced also in 1 ICLR
(1984) pp 317-321

SEPPALA, Christopher: The Pre-Arbitral Procedure for the
Settlement of Disputes in the F.I.D.I.C. (Civil Engineering)
Conditions of Contract 3 ICLR (1986/4, pp 315-337

SINGLETON, Sir Edward: A Proposal for "Instant" Resolution of
Disputes between Contractor/ Engineer/Employer in
Construction Contracts, in: International Business Lawyer
(February 1980), pp 55-59

VILLARD, Michel; BACHELOT, Yves; ROMERO, Jean-Michel: Droit
et pratique des marchés publics de travaux, Paris (Moniteur)
1981, 426 p

VINCENT, Jean and GUINCHARD, Serge: Procédure civile, Paris
(Dalloz) 20th ed 1981 1280 p

WALLACE, Ian N. Duncan: The International Civil Engineering
Contract, London (Sweet & Maxwell) 1974, 197 p, Supplement
1980

WEICK, Günter: Vereinbarte Standardbedingungen im Deutschen
und Englischen Bauvertragsrecht, Munich (Beck) 1977, 283 p

WIEGAND, Christian: Construction Arbitration in the Federal
Republic of Germany 4 ICLR (1987/2) pp 106-125

# ABBREVIATIONS

| | |
|---|---|
| BGB | Bürgerliches Gesetzbuch; German civil Code |
| BLR | Building Law Reports |
| CCAG | Cahier des clauses administratives générales, applicables aux marchés public - Travaux; French public works conditons, last issue 1976 |
| CCAP | Cahier des clauses administratives particulières; conditions of special application in French contracts |
| CTA | Code des tribunaux administratifs; French code of procedure before the administrative tribunals |
| ECE | United Nations Economic Commission for Europe |
| ICC | International Chamber of Commerce |
| ICLR | International Construction Law Review |
| Jahrbuch | Jahrbuch für die Praxis der Schiedsgerichts-barkeit |
| JCT | Joint Contract Tribunal for the Standard Form of Building Contract |
| NCPC | Nouveau Code de procédure civil; French code of civil procedure |
| VOB | Verdingunsordnung für Bauleistungen; German conditions for public and private construction contracts; part A: for awarding contracts; part B: for performance of the work; part C: technical conditions |
| ZPO | Zivilprozessordnung; German Code of civil procedure |

# Discussion on Papers 8–12

DR D. J. O. FERRY, CIRIA, London
   First, I was glad that Ms Craig took a positive view of cost reimbursement (CR). In many quarters these are regarded as dirty words, and people will not face the fact that they are entering into CR arrangements (for example, people try to convince me that management contracting is not CR).
   I would like to emphasize the importance of the procedures and attitudes outlined by Ms Craig, but these are just a necessary on modest projects as on the mega-projects she mentions (though not necessarily involving a firm like KPMG). After all, 10 000 is just as important to the 1 m client as 10 m is to the 1 billion client. However, sometimes the smaller contractors may not perceive the need for client-involved planning and audit as easily as the mega-project contractors, and there may be a need to educate them.
   Second, Ms Craig identified two areas for concern: early payment and improper payment. Would she agree that the latter (by which money is by and large lost forever) is so much more important than the former (where by and large it is not) that if auditing resources are limited they should concentrate on improper payments?

PROFESSOR D. BISHOP, Construction Industry Council, London
   Regarding decennial insurance: one of the consequences of the great restrictions on actions in tort has been the burgeoning of clients' demands for reliable ways of protecting their long term interests. This, and the bargaining strength of possible purchasers and tenants of commercial properties, has led to a sharp increase in the demand for and supply of BUILD-type decennial insurance. There are now about twelve active underwriters in the market with a further group prepared to write material damage insurance for favoured clients, i.e. those with substantial property portfolios.

DISCUSSION

This increase in supply has led to more liberal terms, for example cover is obtainable for engineering services and, in some circumstances, for complete buildings.

DR MARTIN BARNES, <u>Cooper and Lybrand Deloitte, London</u>
May I, from my position in a rival firm, congratulate Alison Craig on an extremely perceptive and comprehensive paper. I would like to draw attention to the striking conformity between her recommendations for giving full weight to the behavioural aspects of project management and the principles which have directed the design of the New Engineering Contract. Similarly, the NEC seeks to help make cost-reimbursable contracts respectable and to encourage their use in the situations where this is the best option for the client.

I would like to know whether it is Ms Craig's opinion that engineering managers are beginning to appreciate more widely the positive contribution that suitably experienced accountants can make to management of engineering projects.

T. H. A. THORNELY, <u>W. S. Atkins Project Management, Epsom</u>
Ms Craig's paper sets out a number of important points which are frequently given insufficient attention in the execution of projects. Among these, cross-national interfaces were mentioned. I would suggest, on the basis of both experience and research for an MBA thesis, that considerable risk and problems can also arise from cross-discipline interfaces: the differences in approach, goals and understanding between the various participants in a project, be they client bodies, engineers, procurers, financiers, insurers, or others.

E. G. TRIMBLE, <u>Loughborough University</u>
With a reimbursable contract, the client has bought a set of resources so he becomes responsible for ensuring that efficiency and productivity are acceptable. Could Ms Craig please amplify her comments on how the client performs this function?

F. GRIFFITHS, <u>Frank Griffiths Associates Ltd, Kebworth Beauchamp</u>
The importance of establishing the appropriate culture and systems, is, I think, well taken. But how and when does the client ensure that the cultures and systems are in place: especially in cost + projects?

R. K. OLIVER, <u>Walter Lawrence Management Ltd, Enfield</u>
The contractor's attitude to cost recovery was

criticized: however, cost control (and cash flow) are frequently complicated by delays in payment, whether directly or as a consequence of action (or inaction) by his advisors. Is this also a mainland European problem?

With respect to the influence of accountants - there has been a trend that those who control the financial side of a project have a greater influence in the control of the works than is justified by their technical competence: will accountants be exempt from this trend?

G. HAWKER, London

I agree that identical words can mean different things in different countries. I would cite the English Law Reform (Miscellaneous Provisions) Act 1934, section 3 of which empowers the Court to award interest whether or not it has been claimed in the pleadings. The section has been enacted in identical words in Northern Ireland and the Republic of Ireland, but whereas in England case law has allowed arbitrators to exercise the power to award interest as if they were a Court, the Northern Ireland judges have refrained from allowing arbitrators to do so if personal injury was involved, while in the Republic of Ireland (whose written Constitution contains a definition of a Court) arbitrators were held not to have such power since an arbitrator was not a Court.

I think that the new draft EC Directive from DG XI, if put into force without drastic amendment, might promote the growth of dummy companies lacking any resources of their own and set up specifically for each project so that, should the liability envisaged by the directive come to pass, instant liquidation of the dummy company could follow, thus protecting the 'parent' company. Any requirement that such liability be covered by insurance would almost certainly fail. In the United Kingdom, 'privatized' control under the Building Regulations by 'approved persons' was introduced a few years ago, but the Act required each 'approved person' to carry appropriate insurance. In the event, no insurers could be found to carry the risk and the system established by the Act was never able to come into force. A further consequence, should the directive be brought into use unamended, might be that contractors would refuse to do anything without prior written instruction from Engineer, Architect or Employer. The Contractor could then claim to be the Employer's (or Engineers's) agent and claim the protection of not being 'independent'.

DISCUSSION

DR C. R. ROBINSON, KMPG Management Consulting, London
    May I first thank Mrs Van Houtte for a very
interesting written contribution and a stimulating
presentation of it.  I was interested to read her
example of the welding subcontractor who was held to be
liable in tort, as I have recently been involved in an
almost identical case in the UK.  This underlines the
fact that there are great similarities in many aspects
of the law in different EC countries, but should not
lull us into the belief that there are not major
differences.
    Much of what Mrs Van Houtte said reinforces the
concept that the most straightforward method of
entering a new market is in partnership with an
organization already active in that market.  Indeed, I
have seen a number of failures arising from going it
alone.
    In the light of what has been said about current
draft directives relating to construction law, is any
change foreseen to the means by which damages awarded
in one country, against an entity with its assets in
another country, may be recovered?

S. B. PRAHL, EEC Services, Rotterdam, The Netherlands
    We have learnt from this interesting presentation
that there are many different legal systems in the EC
and that there are even different interpretations of
the same systems.  Mr Mathurin was requested by the
European Commission to study harmonization.  His report
has been shelved.
    Parallel to this, we see moves from other parties
e.g. consumer organizations through DG XI leading to
the horrifying directive on liability for services with
a safety defect.
    My question is: is it enough to analyse and discuss
the different legal systems, or should the construction
industry join forces and prepare its own proposals
towards the Commission before others (DG XI) start
doing it with counterproductive effects.  We have, as
indicated in the Paper, to increase our lobbying power
in Brussels.

D. E. NEALE, May Gurney & Co Ltd
    In Dr Bunni's assessment of project risks he omitted
to mention two of the very real risks that face
contractors, i.e. risks brought about by the actions or
inactions of engineers.  By undercertification or late
certification of interim accounts an engineer may
seriously damage a contractor's cash flow, thereby
significantly eroding his narrow profit margin.
Similarly, by failing to settle smaller claims - which
the contractor would be unlikely to take to Arbitration
- he could further erode margins.   These risks are

uninsurable but must be taken into account. Does Dr
Bunni believe similar risks exist with other European
contracting practices?

M. SMITH, Swiss Federal Office of Transport, Bern,
Switzerland
   Should we train engineers in risk analysis?

G. HAWKER, London
   Regarding Dr Bunni's paragraph 20 (performance
security): I understood that there were two main types
of performance bond, the 'on demand' type traditionally
provided by banks, and the 'default' type usually
provided by insurance companies. Unlike insurance
companies, banks could until recently keep the capital
value of such bonds out of their balance sheets, and so
were free to lend the capital backing the guarantee to
others, thus making a 'double profit' thereon.
However, a recent international agreement now requires
such guarantees to be brought on to the balance sheet,
and banks have largely ceases issuing such bonds.  Is
there any indication that the insurance companies will
now move in to fill the gap, and start issuing 'on
demand' bonds as well as 'default' bonds?

DR S. CHATTERJEE, Department of Transport, London
   In some projects, cost and time of construction have
been seen to increase very substantially, for example
by 50-100%, due to unforeseen circumstances such as
unexpected geotechnical conditions.  Obviously, the
consulting engineer or the client could not anticipate
such a situation and thus did not make any provision
beforehand.  Cost or time increases of this order could
make the scheme economically non-viable.  The client
may not be able to actually afford such an increase,
and hence may go bankrupt.  There may be external
pressure on a public sector client to abandon such a
scheme in favour of some more worthwhile project.
   Could the Author please indicate whether insurance
against such a situation arising is now available, and
if so at what levels of premium and under what
conditions?  Could he please also advise whether such
insurance policies should be taken out by private
clients or by public organizations, or even a
government department as a risk management measure?

A. LEGGATT, CEDIC, Farnham
   There used to be, and perhaps still is, a 'standard
will form' available in High Street shops for a low
price.  Anyone wishing to make a will simply filled in
the blank spaces and 'voila' - a lawyer's fee had been
saved!  That same standard form was, so the story goes,
the main toast at the Law Society's annual dinner,

being such a prolific source of income for lawyers
resolving the numerous disputes which arose from such a
generalized document.

Although construction contracts are perhaps drafted
with more care and expertise, some of them do seem to
yield a good crop of disputes. I wonder if any of the
eminent international lawyers with us today would be
bold enough to give a 'which' guide to those Contract
Forms which seem to lead to the fewest disputes? Such
advice would be valuable in developing new and improved
forms for the future.

### G. HAWKER, London

I would like to quote Lord Donaldson (Master of the
Rolls) as saying

'It may be that, as a Judge, I have a distorted view
of some aspects of life, but I cannot imagine a civil
engineering contract, particularly one of any size,
which did not give rise to some disputes. This is not
to the discredit of either party to the contract. It
is simply the nature of the beast. What is to their
discredit is if they fail to resolve those disputes as
quickly, economically and sensibly as possible.'*

It is therefore not surprising that the incidence of
arbitrations seems high, and not only in the United
Kingdom, as civil engineering is the same whatever the
country in which it is carried out. Indeed, in my
experience there has been only one instance where there
were no claims at all and the final certificate was the
same as the Tender, but in that case the director
concerned had been embezzling his company's funds and
was desperate to get his hands on the money.

A recent case in England cast doubt on the efficacy
of using an 'adjudicator'. A subcontractor thought
that he was being under-paid and called in the
adjudicator under the JCT Form of Subcontract. The
Adjudicator found for the subcontractor, but the main
contractor considered his award too generous and would
not pay. The Court later ruled that the Adjudicator's
award was not enforceable by the Court. Thus, it now
seems open to the party ordered to pay money by an
Adjudicator simple to aver that the award was mistaken,
and thereby abort the whole procedure.

While the concept of bringing in a neutral 'outsider'
to resolve disputes during the currency of a prrject
seems attractive, I foresee difficulties if such a
system were to come into general use, simply because
sufficient appropriately qualified and experienced
persons might not be available to perform such
functions. For the best results, such 'neutrals'

---

*Foreword to 'The ICE Arbitration Practice' (1986) by Hawker, Uff
and Timms. Thomas Telford, London.

should be appointed at the start of a project and should keep in touch with it so as to save time when problems arose. The number of persons able and willing to take on such tasks is unlikely to match the number of projects calling for their services.

The Institution of Civil Engineers has had a set of conciliation rules in place for some years, Sixth Edition of the ICE Conditions of Contract contains a 'conciliation option' in addition to the reference back to the Engineer for a decision under Clause 66(1) and eventual arbitration. Within the United Kingdom there is already some confusion with regard to nomenclature, as the terms 'conciliator', Mediator', adjudicator' and 'neutral' seem to mean different things to different bodies. The British Academy of Experts is in the course of setting up an ad hoc interdisciplinary working party to consider and make recommendations on the meanings to be given to these various terms and the functions which each should perform; it is to be hoped that the Institution's use of 'conciliator' will carry the day. The Academy is also now offering training courses for would-be 'neutrals', as is the Centre for European Dispute Resolution, a private venture launched by a number of large professional firms and companies. The Institution is hoping to co-operate with the Academy, the Centre and other bodies such as the Chartered Institute of Arbitrators in all these matters.

As for arbitration, I see the major problem as being delay: delay in getting an arbitration going, delay which almost always follows the involvement of lawyers, and delay arising from reluctant respondents trying to impede an arbitration or stop it completely. The ICE Arbitration Procedure (1983) strengthened the powers of the arbitrator to encourage progress, and the privately-funded working party at present drafting a consolidated Arbitration Bill (for England and Wales) is being urged to write in similar powers. Effective solutions are, however, very difficult to achieve. One recent example on a major international project concerned a massive performance bond. The contractors would not accept an 'on demand' bond and the promoters could not countenance the normal inevitable delay in establishing their right to call in a 'default' bond. The solution attempted was the establishment of a special arbitration provision so that the issue of alleged default could be heard and an award issued within 42 days, with total exclusion of reference to or review by any Court. As yet, this procedure has not been activated, so its degree of success in achieving its objectives cannot be assessed. However, the price of speed was the imposition of draconic interlocutory time limits and constraints and the immediate establishment of a panel of prospective arbitrators,

while the freedom from Court interference was sought by
providing that the arbitration should take place in
Belgium, since, as all parties to the contract were
from countries outside Belgium, the Belgian Courts
ought to lack jurisdiction. If the worse came to the
worst, it would be interesting to see what happens.

J. E. WALLACE, Enco Civil Engineering Ltd, Slough
   Dr Bunni mentioned 71 risks (Fig. 1, p 00), and asked
that Professor Perry and others should do more research
into risk. I suggest that theory and practice are two
different things: if, as John Armitt stated, the 'mark
up' by contractors on net costs today is very low, I
would also suggest that if my company and Laing had
computer programmes etc. examining the 'risk', we would
end up marking ourselves out of the market and would
have no work - civil engineering contracting is a risky
business!
   I always thought that it 'takes two to tango'. Why
is it that in discussions on risks and claims the
scenario always ends up like a western movie, with 'the
baddies' being the contractors and 'the goodies' being
'the rest'! A contract is between the Client and the
Contractor, but the disputes are mostly blamed on the
Contractor. I have experienced an arbitration where
the Client disputes the Engineer's decision.
Contractors only get paid what they are entitled to
under the contract - unfortunately, often only after
disputes, claims and arbitration many months or years
after the event.

DR M. BARNES, Coopers and Lybrand Deloitte, London
   The four week period for an Adjudicator's decision on
a dispute, specified in the New Engineering Contract,
is not as harsh as it may appear at first. Remember
that the adjudicator is on the scene from the
beginning, if only in the background, and also that
other procedures set out in the NEC will usually ensure
that all the information he needs will have been
assembled ready for him. This is why we expect four
weeks usually to be quite long enough. May I also
point out that the contractor is not obliged to bring
an affected subcontractor into the matter. The NEC
allows it but does not require it.

A. CRAIG, Paper 8
   Dr Ferry has identified quite rightly that the
attitudes and procedures required on mega-projects that
I have outlined in my paper are just as appropriate on
more modest projects. It is a question of resources,
which brings in Dr Ferry's second good point about the
relative importance of checking for payments that are
made improperly compared to payments made early. All

the 'project audit' tests described in my paper (both
the compliance type of test and the substantive tests)
have improper expenditure as their prime focus.
Testing is designed to check that a cost is 'proper'.
This usually means that, among other things, an invoice
has been properly rendered, is for valid goods or
services, and has been processed in a proper fashion.
By contrast, checking the timing of the contractor's
cash outflows is a minor issue! Nevertheless benefits
could be conferred on related companies over the length
of a major project by a contractor making payments
earlier than officially due. The balance of testing,
between checking the fundamental properness of the
costs, and checking other issues such as the timing of
the eventual cash flow, needs to be weighed against the
relative risks on the particular project and the
resources and financial expertise available to do the
checking.

I would like to thank Dr Barnes for his kind words on
my paper. I also welcome his comments about the New
Engineering Contract. As far as I am concerned, I look
forward to being involved with a form of contract that
at last takes into account the behavioural imperatives
in project management. To me, the behavioural aspects
are crucial. The cost reimbursable contract,
appropriate perhaps infrequently, is therefore an
option to be considered. This is especially the case
where there are major risks to be shared, and where
significant incentives can also be built into the terms.

To respond to Dr Barnes' question about engineering
managers appreciating the positive contribution that
suitably experienced accountants can make to the
management of engineering projects, yes I do think that
the appreciation is growing. It is a question of
specialisms. An accounting-trained person has a useful
contribution to make in areas such as financial
controls and management information systems, working
alongside engineers with their technical expertise.
However I must emphasize Dr Barnes' description
'suitably experienced' - any accountant who gets
involved must understand the industry and the way it
operates before venturing on site and expecting to be
listened to!

In reply to Mr Thornley, many important points have
come out in this conference, and I have touched on just
a few of them in my paper. In particular I mentioned
the difficulties of cross-national interfaces; from my
experience it is astonishingly difficult to get
effective cooperation across national borders without a
lot of time spent looking after the quality of that
interface. This is mainly about people, and cultural
differences, but it is also about languages, the
technology embodied in the communications software and

hardware, the project management disciplines, and even
the specific roles and budget responsibilities that
different countries expect!

The questioner rightly points out that
cross-discipline differences can arise on a project and
can generate heat and dissent quite out of proportion
to the size of the issue.  All projects are uniquely
different, and what worked on one may not necessarily
work on another.  All parties need to be willing to
learn from others, to cross-fertilize ideas between
disciplines and to work as a team for a mutual goal.
The real challenge comes when you have both
cross-discipline and cross-national issues to deal with
together in one mega-project!  the important thing is
to be aware of the difficulties and to treat with care
the individuals whose beliefs and behaviours are being
challenged.

In response to Mr Trimble, the role of the client is
never easy.  On a reimbursable contract he has bought a
set of resources and, as you say, becomes responsible
for ensuring that efficiency and productivity are
acceptable.  Firstly he must have a good project
management information system that tells him what is
happening, where the bottlenecks are, how the resources
are planned, what the costs are versus progress to
date, and suitable time and cost projections.  And
secondly he must have a good line of communication to
all who are involved on his project.  He needs to be
very sure of his requirements - or as sure as the
design development will let him be - and very clear in
his communication of those requirements.  He needs to
be able to trust the people he has working for him.
And he needs to monitor the progress rigorously (or
employ others to do so who can report on problems
swiftly in the way he needs) and take swift and
effective follow-up action when problems loom on the
horizon.  It all looks easy enough, but it is very
difficult to do in practice!

Concerning Mr Griffiths' question, how does a client
ensure that appropriate cultures and systems are in
place?  Let me take culture first.  By being sensitive
to the cultural issues at stake, the client can take
steps to set up the project in such a way as to
minimize friction.  If a project is a joint project
between two countries, the use of both nationalities of
staff, combined ...th language training for those not
already bilingual, can help to ease the cultural
integration.  The adoption of suitably compatible
personnel policies can do much to ease the 'people'
situation, although one should beware of ending up with
a salary and benefits structure that has to be better
than either country and is therefore very expensive!
When should this 'cultural planning' be done?  At the

very earliest opportunity. And it must be supported, and be seen to be supported, from the top.

Regarding systems, if none of the parties to the project can contribute suitable project management and control systems then advice should be sought at the very earliest opportunity. Strict adherence to project control disciplines, and audit if appropriate, helps establish working relationships and the lines of communication as soon as possible in the negotiations.

To Mr Oliver, delay in payment is also a European problem - even now some of the heads of industry in Europe are calling for swifter payment of suppliers and contractors/ subcontractors. The role of advisers here can, as you suggest, sometimes contribute to a delay in payment from the client; for instance if there is a potential claim, lawyers may advise that payment be withheld pending further investigation. However cash is the lifeblood of any organization; a contractor is no different, and arbitrary withholding of payments is unfair and usually unwarranted. I have found that many of the instances of late payment are actually due to a failure in communication, for instance the contractor not warning his client of a change in the cash flow pattern this month, and explaining the reasons to him before expecting him to part with the cash. 'No surprises' is a good rule of thumb for a contractor expecting to get paid swiftly by his client.

With regard to your second point, accountants are unlikely ever to control or even significantly influence the control of the works on construction and engineering projects! However I do think we can play a useful role in helping think through the relative risks, establish and then monitor the project financial controls, and information systems, and possibly audit the reimbursable costs. I certainly hope that our skills and, occasionally, insights will be put to good use in the future.

V. VAN HOUTTE, Paper 10

Since the submission of my paper, new developments have superseded the information given under 35 above, concerning the liability for services. Indeed, on 18 January 1991 a proposal for a directive was published which, if adopted as presently drafted, will not only harmonize - at least to some extent - the construction liability rules in the European Community, but will greatly innovate in the field of construction liability. The main principles of the proposal are

(a) the supplier of a service is liable for certain damages caused by him
(b) the burden of proof lies on the supplier; he must prove that he did not commit a fault. The injured

person must only prove his damage and its causal
relationship with the performance of the service
(c) if more than one supplier is liable, the liability
is joint and several
(d) liability exists as a rule during 5 years after
the provision of the service, except when the service
relates to the design or construction of immovable
property, in which case it exists during 20 years
(e) the limitation period for proceedings is in
principle three years, but for construction-related
services 10 years, after the day on which the
plaintiff becomes aware or should reasonably have
become aware of the damage, the service and the
identity of the supplier
(f) the liability may not be restricted or excluded.

The proposal raises numerous questions.

(a) It is based on article 100a of the Treaty of Rome.
Still, its aim appears to be more to innovate in the
national legislations, than to harmonize them. The
Commission has not brought evidence that if there is
relatively little transnational construction activity
this is caused by the difference in liability rules.
If the Commission's first aim is to protect the
consumers and if the Commission goes beyond
harmonizing different existing rules because they
form a barrier to trade, as it does in this proposal,
it is questionable whether article 100a is the proper
legal basis for the directive.
(b) The proposal does not abandon the principle of
liability for fault - as opposed to strict liability
which was introduced by the defective product
liability directive. However, the reversal of the
burden of proof creates a liability system which is
almost as hard on the suppliers of services as strict
liability. The supplier will have to bring the
negative evidence that he did not commit a
negligence. In many cases, this will be impossible.
(c) 'Fault' is to be assessed, according to the
directive, in relation to the safety which may
reasonably be expected. There is no indication whose
standard of reasonable expectation of safety will be
applied. The general public's? Or the specific
consumer's? If the latter, there appears to be a
contradiction contained in this article 1.3 which
seems to indicate that the supplier may warn the
consumer about certain dangers of the service,
thereby reducing the expectations of the consumer and
his level of liability, on the one hand, and article
7 of the proposal, prohibiting the supplier to limit
his liability.
(d) Damage is defined as

(i) death or other direct damage to the health or physical integrity of persons

(ii)direct damage to property, which is normally intended for private use and was actually intended for or used by the injured person principally for private use, and

(iii) financial damage resulting directly from (a) and (b).

This restrictive definition of damage confirms the directive's aim to protect consumers. Only 'private' damage is recoverable under the proposal. The consequence will be that the directive's principle will apply only to some of the damages caused by the negligence of the supplier: damage to, for example, an office or commercial building will not be covered. Or, for example, damage caused by a collapsing garage roof to a private car will be covered by the directive, the damage to the commercial truck standing next to it not. The result will be that the contractor or designer of the garage roof may be liable for the damage to the private car (because he was not able to prove that he did not commit a fault), but would not be liable for damage to the truck because the owner of the truck could not prove that the roof collapsed because of the contractor's or designer's negligence.

(e)The proposal creates joint and several liability when several people are liable for the damage. The principle of joint and several liability is severally criticized in those national systems where it exists. Its consequence is that parties which otherwise have no joint interest and often do not even know each other, are to guarantee to the consumer of the service not only each other's professional competence but even each other's solvability. The protection of the consumer does not need to go as far as totransfer the risk of bankruptcy of one of his service suppliers to his other service suppliers.

(f)The relationship between articles 9 and 10 is not clear: is the period of liability of 20 years to be cumulated with the 10 years limitation period? Would the directive hold the supplier of a construction-related service liable during 29 years, provided proceedings have been started before the end of the 20th year following provision of the service?

(g)It is doubtful whether the consumer is helped in any way by such unreasonably long periods of liability and limitation. Most construction damages become apparent within the five first years following construction, and do not justify liability periods of more than 10 years. The reversal of the burden of proof, combined with the above mentioned long periods will lead to a considerable increase of insurance premiums, if it does not make insurance unavailable.

The increased insurance cost will ultimately be added to the price of the service. Furthermore, the suppliers of services will become defensive instead of innovative in their work, they will spend more time on creating evidence of their diligence, and the relationship of trust between client and service supplier will be lost.

In conclusion, the proposal goes beyond a harmonization; it creates entirely new rules but without concern for the need for coherence of liability rules for construction as a whole (as it covers only 'private; damages). The need of consumers for more protection has been misunderstood. They would be better off with more quality control, easier access to courts, specialized arbitration, small claims courts, better and more standard contracts, and a well-balanced system of construction project insurance.

In reply to Mr Robinson, since the United Kingdom, Ireland and Denmark have also ratified the Convention of Brussels on jurisdiction and the enforcements of judgements in civil and commercial matters, the recovery under a judgement of a court from an EC country in any of the other EC countries should no longer create particular problems (except in Spain and Portugal). With the exception of these two states, a judgement given in any of the EC member states can be enforced in another member state if

(a) it is enforceable in the first member state

(b) it is declared enforceable in the second

The second state may refuse to declare the judgement enforceable exclusively for very specific reasons (e.g. infringement of its local public policy or of the rights of defence).

In reply to Mr Prahl, the construction industry and construction professionals could indeed take usefulinitiatives to reduce the number of legal procedures in construction. Improvement of contract drafting, increased use of high-quality standard contracts, quality assurance of design services, improved communication with clients and with other parties on the construction site, publication of maintenance manuals, use of a dispute avoidance mechanism, are all measures which may contribute to a better situation for the consumers of the construction industry and can be initiated by the professionals themselves. In any case, the professional associations should stay in close contact with the Brussels legislators to ascertain that the specificities of their trade or profession are fully taken into account when legislative measures are being prepared.

# 13. Opening the internal market on the construction sector

R. CARONNA, Commission of the European Communities

SYNOPSIS. The European Commission, prompted by the wide discrepancies in technology, law and standards which still dominate the construction industry in Community countries, creating numerous impediments to the exchange and free movement of personnel, goods and services and also leading to very limited consumer protection, has drawn up a vast harmonisation programme aiming to open up the Single Market within the industry.

1. The history of European construction, its successes and crises, are mirrored in the long-standing conflict between the desire for economic and political integration within the Community and the concern of its member states to preserve their national sovereignty.

The aim of creating a Single Market, as defined by the Treaty of Rome in 1957, has been achieved in part by the abolition of customs' barriers.

But, if regulations governing economic competition are to play their vital unifying role, the creation of a truly common market demands the corresponding abolition of physical, technical and tax barriers.

While tangible progress has been made in this direction, attempts to relaunch European construction during the 1970's have not quite hit the mark. However, the cost of non-unification in Europe falls within a bracket of 170 to 250 billion Ecus a year for companies and member states.

As a result, the European Commission, on the initiative of its President, Jacques Delors, drafted a 'white paper' which defines a strategy and time-table for achieving the single market.

The aim is at once ambitious and motivating: this is the buffer for 1992 - to overturn the established, to give the continent of Europe a new frontier and between now and 31st December 1992 to remove anything which impedes the free movement of people, goods, services and capital.

A real challenge is involved in the creation of a genuine Single Market of 325 million consumers.

We need a coherent strategy in that its aim must to be to achieve a common market as such, but also serve other objectives, such as the establishment of a market which is both expanding and flexible.

It must not only remove obstacles to free exchange such as physical, technical and tax barriers, but do this is such a way as to increase the effectiveness of company competition and, consequently, increase prosperity and create jobs. It is expected that 1992* will have a positive impact on employment in the medium term creating around 2 million jobs.

This legislative programme was strengthened by the single European Act which came into force on the 1st July 1987.  This brings under one law provisions reforming European Institutions, the extension of the Commission's field of competence and provisions on European cooperation in foreign policy.

Henceforth, the rule on unanimity becomes the exception and the European Council takes a majority decision on the proposals of the Commission in conjunction with the European Parliament.  However, it should be noted, on the decision of the Council, that unanimity is required for decisions concerning the free movement of persons and the rights and interests of employees.

2. I wanted to touch very briefly on the current situation of Europe and its perspectives, as this is the context to our industry, construction, and

---

* Translators note: Most European countries use '1993' to denote the date of introduction of the single European market, in the UK '1992' is used.

the theme of your Conference, "Construction without
frontiers".
In fact, with a view to contributing to the
development of the Community, the Commission
outlined a series of actions in its White Paper on
achieving the Single Market, which are directly
concerned with the construction industry.

3.  However, before discussing these, I think it
might be useful to locate our industry within the
general economic context.

The construction industry in Europe:

- employs around 7 million people.  There are also
thought to be more than 40 million people directly
or indirectly dependent on the construction
industry, that is one European in eight.  It is by
far and away the largest European employer.
Unfortunately the industry has about one million
people out of work.

- has a knock-on effect on employment and further
economic development to an extent of 50%
(multipliers of 1.5 to 2 depending on the country).
In fact, it affects a large number of industries,
services and professionals both upstream and
downstream whether wholly or partially.

- achieves a turnover in the order of 370 billion
Ecus.

- its Gross Domestic Product is around 8 to 9%.

- is largely made up of small-sized companies.

- investments aside, it creates more employment
than any other manufacturing industry.

- it cannot benefit from internal economies (or
economies of scale) or from external economies (or
economies from its location)  which usually benefit
the manufacturing industry.  Each construction
project is unique and must be carried out where it
is required, not in the most beneficial location.
Furthermore, there is no regularity or continuity
of activity, which has caused the steady fall in
productivity in construction compared to other
industries and the relatively higher costs of its
products.

Productivity in the industry has increased by an
annual average of 1.9% between 1970 and 1987

compared to a general industrial average of 2.3%,
and 3.4% in the manufacturing industry, 4.5% in
energy production and 4.8% in agriculture.

- a slight drop in demand for new housing must be
expected in all EC member states.

This prognosis of a slow-down in new construction
must however be tempered by:

. an increase in the quality demanded;
. a more varied demand which aims at correcting
local imbalances, particularly in larger towns
where there is a constant need for intermediate
local housing;
. greater attention to renovating existing sites
(here the United Kingdom and Scandinavia have
provided good examples).

4. This data on the characteristics of the European
construction industry, its size, complexity and
social role, has long been an important focus of
the Commission whose aim is to:

- promote the creation of a technical, legislative
and economic fabric essential for the development
of the industry;

- improve the quality of construction;

- achieve a vast single market in which everyone:
designers, developers, builders, consultants,
inspectors and insurers can conduct their
activities without restraints or obstacles arising
from different national provisions;

- protect the end user of the product resulting
from the building activity.

5.   To this end, the Community adopted **Directive
89/106 on the unification of legislative,
regulatory and administrative provisions of member
states regarding construction products.**

I do not wish to dwell too long on the content and
implications of the Directive, but I think it would
be useful to stress certain important aspects.

This a fundamental piece of legislation which when
applied will have a decisive impact on the majority
of building and civil engineering projects and
regulations and will soon be transposed into the
legislation of members states (end June 1991).

Its aim is clear: to remove the technical and legal obstacles which impede free movement and hinder the use of construction products originating from one member state in another.

Its basic requirements cover mechanical resistance and stability; safety in the event of fire; hygiene, health, environment; safe practice; noise protection; energy conservation and heat insulation. They are defined in terms of objectives.

**Directive 85/384 is concerned with the mutual recognition of diplomas, certificates and other qualifications in architecture** and includes measures to promote the practical application of the right to establish this important category of professionals. The Directive is accompanied by a Decision and a Recommendation.

**Directive 89/440 is concerned with the coordination of legislative, regulatory and administrative provisions on the application of rules within the framework of procedures for concluding public works contracts.**

It provides for strengthening conditions of competition through a procedure of prior information and extending publication deadlines for invitations to tender as well as establishing clearer procedures. It determines specific conditions for markets with a threshold greater than 5 million Ecus and excluded sectors.

**Directive 88/295 is concerned with the coordination of legislative, regulatory and administrative provisions relating to the application of rules within the framework of procedures for concluding public supplies contracts.**

It strengthens regulations on prior information relating to these contracts and requires that reference be made to community standards where they exist.

It provides for control of the specific suitability of suppliers on the basis of two criteria relating, respectively, to their financial suitability and their technical suitability.

**Directive 89/665 is concerned with the coordination of legislative, regulatory and administrative provisions relating to the application of appeals**

procedures regarding public supplies and works' contracts.

By 21st December 1991, Community member states should have established rights of appeal for injured parties resulting from failure to apply supply and employment contracts.

**Directive 87/374 relates to the unification of legal, regulatory and administrative provisions of member states on liability for faulty products.**

This directive aims to remove the legal discrepancies which distort conditions of competition and to provide better consumer protection by simplifying the application process for compensation.

This directive is concerned with goods used in industrial production and also goods used for building works or incorporated into buildings.

Eurocodes relating to reinforced concrete structures, steel structures, structures combining steel and concrete, wooden structures, brick structures, foundations, para-seismic structures and a specific code for actions which, under the newly formed Technical Committee of the European Committee for Standardisation will replace of Eurocode 1 (General).

In applying the conclusions of the 1984 Council on the European policy of standardisation and in agreement with member states and interested parties, Eurocodes have been incorporated into standardisation and transferred to the European Committee for Standardisation. Eurocodes will serve as:

- a means of demonstrating the conformity of civil engineering works and building with the first basic requirement of the Products and Construction Directive (mechanical resistance and stability).

- a base for specific contracts on the execution of public and private construction works.

The proposed Directive on "Excluded Sectors".

This concerns supply and works contracts within the four sectors previously excluded by the directives adopted in 1971, 1977, 1988 and 1989 (energy, transport, water and telecommunications) exceeding

a threshold of 400,000 Ecus for supplies and 5
million Ecus for works. However, for supply
contracts relating to telecommunications the
threshold rises to 600,000 Ecus.

However, certain activities particular to the
drinking water network and to air and sea transport
and energy still do not fall within the directive's
field of application.

The proposed directive was improved in principle
during the 'Single Market' meeting of the Council
of Ministers on 22nd February 1990.

6 I have outlined the principal characteristics and
objectives of the directives, draft directives and
codes drawn up to date insofar as they relate to
the construction industry and its development both
upstream in tackling what we would call "technical"
aspects (Building Product Directives, Eurocodes,
Directive on liability for faulty products), and
downstream, for legal and regulatory aspects
concerning the free movement of personnel and the
introduction of the Single market (Architects
Directives, Public Works and Supplies Contracts
Directives and associated Directives - Excluded
sectors and Appeals procedures).

But I believe that if we really wish to establish a
single European market within our industry, improve
the quality of construction, protect the end-user
of the construction "product", permit the free
movement of various professionals, contractors and
capital, the market should be subject to minimum,
but uniform, regulation for the whole of the
construction industry.

In fact, I believe that without this essential
basis, any individual or legal entity originating
from our member countries will encounter
considerable difficulties in moving about freely
and carrying out their activities in another
country, so all the measures taken to date will not
achieve the aims desired when the various
directives were drafted and adopted.

It was for this reason that the Commission
initially wanted to familiarise itself with the
current situation in Community countries before
adopting any measures.

In 1987, the Commission appointed an independent
expert to act as consultant, to analyse the

national systems in force in the construction
industry, focusing particular attention on:

- the legal basis
- regulations
- controls
- professions
- contracts
- liability
- guarantees
- insurance

and where applicable:

- disputes and arbitration.

The results of the study, issued to interested
parties in 1988, revealed that the principal
differences relate to the following areas:

- public control of construction
- the role of the main participants
- laws and regulations of enforcement
- decentralisation
- supervision of operations
- the role and responsibility of architects
- technical services
- the competence of participants
- sub-contracting
- jurisdiction and legislation
- contractor liability
- project management liability
- the burden of proof
- post-construction responsibility
- protection for house buyers
- professional liability insurance.

On the basis of these findings, the Commission
extended the consultant's assignment in 1988,
requesting him to:

- assess the advantages and disadvantages of
different national systems

- establish a community model for guarantees and
insurance for the construction industry

- advise on the possible impact the objectives of
the study may have on achieving the Single Market
and on the application of the following community
directives; 89/106/EEC, relating to the unification
of legal, regulatory and administrative provisions
of member states regarding Construction Products;

and 71/305/EEC, relating to the coordination of procedures for concluding Public works contracts, modified by Directive 89/440/EEC.

According to the results from the second stage of the study, which were published and distributed to interested parties in 1989, the free movement of goods and services in the construction industry can be achieved more easily if in addition to the following areas of harmonisation:

- basic requirements
- the role of participants
- plans and specifications
- invitations to tender,

(subjects on which the Commission has already taken action and has already obtained results)
the following subjects are also harmonised:

- liability
- guarantees
- insurance
- supervision of operations

**The aim is to provide standard guarantees to owners and builders when carrying out work and above all following their completion.**

The proposals formulated in the second stage of the study, which are based on the finding that few countries possess truly satisfactory legal systems and there are many loopholes, ambiguities, complications and discrepancies relating to the following six objectives:

- to define the principal duties of those involved in construction

- to harmonise the supervision of construction based on the six basic requirements of the "Building Products" Directive,

- standard liability, adapted to the duties of those involved in construction

- a minimum general guarantee of delivery and good quality workmanship

- the insurance of high quality, providing consumer protection for the purchasers of new housing

- improving relations between all those involved.

THE FUTURE

These proposals also indicate fifteen subjects
which could be integrated into a community system
and formulate possible solutions.

Analysis of the full study results confirms my
previous assertions.  That is, if we really want to
achieve, on the one hand, the basic conditions to
protect the end user of the construction industry's
"product" and, on the other hand, to promote the
Single Market within the industry, the importance
of which has already been stressed, the Community
must create firm legal and regulatory bases to
remove the national differences that give rise to a
multitude of complications and difficulties, are a
source of misunderstandings and disputes and
discourage customers and people employed in the
construction industry.

These factors give rise to considerable problems
within one country and take on a more serious
nature when those working on a construction project
and 'customers' originate from different
countries.

However,

- the importance of the industry and the interests
at stake

- the number of people involved in the construction
process and the diversity of industries and related
professionals,

- the realisation that any harmonisation would
affect the laws, traditions and principles of law
upon which the relevant national legal systems,

**call for caution before embarking on the
harmonisation envisaged in the study without, of
course, losing sight of the Treaty objectives.**

We have, therefore, thought it advisable to:

- establish bilateral contacts and consult some
national professional organisations, particularly
builders and developers, to collate their opinions,
on the one hand, on the advisability of proceeding
with the harmonisation of the areas in question,
and on the other hand, which areas (from those
suggested in the study) should be given priority:

- having consulted the above, to organise a meeting
with the Information Management Regulations Group

for construction, confined to experts and
representatives of the member states[1].

The opinions expressed at the meeting, along with
those that emerged from the study and the bilateral
meetings, allow an evaluation of the real
likelihood of the success of the planned
harmonisation and the priority to be allocated to
the areas proposed in the study.

Community action will depend on what is decided.
Therefore, in the rest of my presentation I shall
use conditional verbs and adverbs such as
"possibly".

However, we may draw some conclusions and formulate
guidelines for future action.

In fact, as regards contacts with professional
organisations in some countries, in the clear
majority of cases, contributors reiterated the
opportunity to achieve some degree of harmonisation
of the legislative aspects of the construction
industry, the objectives being to establish a
single market within the industry, to further
protect the 'end-user' of the 'product' of this
industry and to improve the mobility of citizens.

Furthermore, except for certain areas which are of
interest to the whole of the construction industry
(civil engineering and residential building),
priority should be given to building, particularly
residential.

Consequently, adopting the fifteen subjects
proposed in the study, community harmonisation
could relate to:

- the construction industry in general (civil
engineering and building, whether residential or
not):

- the construction process: terminology and
definitions
- the qualification of those involved in
construction

1 This meeting will be held during the period
between writing this presentation and the date of
the Conference. Consequently, the rest of this
talk is drafted on the basis of the results
obtained before the meeting with GRIM. Any
modifications and updates will be communicated
verbally by the author at the Conference.

- sub-contracting
- supervision of construction
- permanent conciliation and technical expertise
- acceptance
- liability

as regards the sub-sector of residential building only:

- legal guarantees
- financial cover for the legal guarantee.

The form that community harmonisation will take could vary according to the subjects treated. For each subject or for each group of related subjects, one would draw up either a code of good conduct, a Recommendation, a Directive or a community Regulation.

However, from contacts with professional organisations, I have been able to detect a desire that at least the following subjects, concerning acceptance of work, liability, legal guarantee and financial cover for this guarantee, limited to the sector of residential building, should be covered by a Community Directive or Regulation.

7 Obviously the choice of solutions will depend on whether or not there is a desire to arrive at solutions which are binding and really effective, particularly as regards the last four subjects where drawing up the corresponding legislation will not differ substantially from one solution to another.

This choice must also take into account the "Subsidiary Principle" under which the EC may only legislate when the provisions at Community level are essential or preferable in relation to national provisions.

If the form chosen is the Community Directive, a longer than usual transition period could be provided, particularly for the last four subjects, to take into account the difficulties that member states may encounter in transposing this directive into their national legislation and familiarising the various interested parties with the resulting new legal systems.

It is clear that any legal form (Regulation, Directive, Recommendation) or other form (Code of good conduct or professional agreement) chosen must also be examined for conformity with Treaty articles and the Single European Act.

Whatever form is chosen, a code of good conduct, professional agreement, recommendation, directive or regulation, the objectives to be pursued for each area should be:

**For the construction process: terminology and definitions:**

- to develop a common language, limited to a number of important terms, in close liaison with the permanent committee of the "Construction Products Directive";

- to identify and define the principal construction processes, without, however, excluding the use of other processes;

- to define the principal duties and roles fulfilled by the most important people in the construction process (foremen, designers, contractors, inspectors) whatever the process selected and the sub-sector concerned (public or private works).

This subject would relate to both public and private construction.

**For the qualifications of people involved in construction:**

- to define the standard criteria for qualifications to achieve high quality and to avoid any abuse when selecting personnel for any construction process and particularly for Community invitations to tender.

It is clear that this would also contribute to a better application of the "Public Works Contracts" Directive of the Communication of the Commission to the Council on 15th June 1989 on "A general approach to certification and testing" and the Directive entitled "Public contracts - Excluded Sectors".

**For sub-contracting:**

- according to the Council's Resolution of 26th September 1989, on the development of sub-contracting within the Community, to define the reciprocal rights and duties in  sub-contracting which, at the present time, fulfills a very important function in relation to the free market and in the construction process.

**For the inspection of construction processes:**

- to define certain essential principles, by resuming the ideas and concepts of the "Construction Products" Directive, to contribute to the safety of building operations and to enforce requirements, while permitting a certain amount of self-monitoring;

**For permanent conciliation and technical expertise:**

- to define the activities of the people involved who should, in any case, be selected jointly by the interested parties, to avoid disagreements, disputes, conflicts and civil procedures and any factors which prevent the smooth operation of a site, both during construction and the legal guarantee period;

**For acceptance:**

- to define the legal significance, consequences and forms of acceptance;

**For liability, legal guarantee and the financial cover of the legal guarantee:**

- to define the systems, based on standard criteria of time-scales, duration, stability and simplicity so that they may represent a just balance between the different national systems and satisfy the various people involved in the construction project as well as the "end users", the customers of "products" resulting from the construction project.

Furthermore, for "financial cover and legal guarantee", the corresponding system must allow interested parties the opportunity to select the best adapted formula from those available (for example: insurance, bank guarantee, "bonds", security, solid guarantee of the relevant interested parties).

8 How does the Commission intend to proceed in drawing up these texts?

For each subject or area of related subjects selected for harmonisation, the Commission would form working groups composed of government experts and professionals from every discipline concerned, responsible for establishing the preliminary drafts of the corresponding Codes of good conduct and/or Recommendations and/or Directives and/or Regulations.

Furthermore, for certain subjects, the Commission may entrust this task to European professional organisations in the relevant fields that are willing to assist.

We are relying heavily on this direct cooperation with professional organisations, as they can contribute their experience and knowledge of the field concerned. They are in a unique position to inform us of the needs of their members and the specific problems to be resolved and, it should also be said, they alone will be able to offer the assistance of qualified and experienced people, vital to the success of any undertaking.

9 I should like to conclude my presentation with this message:

Your Institution will be involved through the European Federation of your profession, along with all the other organisations directly involved in construction, in the community process of drafting legislation. We are sure that you will treat this in a spirit of positive cooperation bearing in mind that 1992 constitutes a welcome invitation to the whole of the construction industry to seize the future with confidence while not neglecting any of the community dimensions of the problems it faces.

Let us not forget that if we wish to achieve construction without frontiers, as indicated by the title of this conference, a fabric of provisions and harmonised legal and technical standards is essential. Otherwise financial and professional operations will encounter profound difficulties in exercising their activities within the Community.

We will only achieve this directive through determination, perseverance and by abandoning national prejudices, failing which both a Europe without frontiers and construction without frontiers will remain beautiful, but empty words.

# 14. The European engineer: education and training

J. MICHEL, Ecole Nationale des Ponts et Chaussées

SYNOPSIS. How will the future European Engineer be educated
and trained ? To this complex question, it is proposed to answer
by examining three main components of the development of engineering education : the historical and cultural basis, the
two last decades tendencies and the very recent European trends
and perspectives.
    The internal European debate opens a larger one which puts
emphasis on the role of the engineer in the modern society and
in a more and more international world.

INTRODUCTION
    The next years will constitute an important hinge for Europe.
They certainly will be essential for the engineer, for his or
her professional activity as well as for his or her formation.
The beginning of the 90's decade is the issue of a long set of
efforts that have been realized within Europe for developing a
true European view on the engineer'future.
    As early as 1950 was founded FEANI -the European Federation
of National Engineering Associations-, which allowed to ini-
tiate a recognition of the different types or profiles of engineers working in Europe.
    More recently, SEFI -the European Society for Engineering
Education-, founded in 1973 by some well-known specialists of
engineering education, considered as an essential goal to
develop a mutual understanding of the various systems of education and training of European engineers.
    It seems to be clear now that it exists a need of conver-
gency for more "comparability" and more "compatibility". Thus
the recent creation by FEANI of the European Title EUR. ING.,
as well as the impact of European programmes such as ERASMUS,
COMETT, LINGUA, or TEMPUS, provide good testimonies of the
will to increase the European mobility, especially in the fields
of engineering activity and engineering formation.
    But, what kind of engineers for the future open Europe ?
    And what kind of education and training ?
    One will try to propose here some useful answers to these
questions. They will be based on a search for understanding the
key-word "European diversity" as well as on the respect of the
cultural and historical development of each national country
and society.

# THE FUTURE

## THE HISTORICAL AND CULTURAL BASIS

Engineers exist in Europe since more than three centuries. Engineering schools have been progressively founded since the beginning of the 18th Century (Prague 1707, Paris Ecole Royale des Ponts et Chaussées 1747, etc...). There is an historical heritage, that has to be assumed. One must clearly be conscious of the extraordinary richess of the past related to engineers and one must not sell off this historical dimension for some brillant Euro-technocratic activism.

Engineers have been educated and trained through various ways within the various European countries, in relation with the national cultural models of development of the society. In other words, engineers'activity and formation that exist to day are the result of specific socio-cultural determinations. To discuss the future of engineering education and training without taking into consideration this socio-cultural dimension and the diversity of the national models would be a regrettable error.

Three main canonical models can be envisaged in a first analysis ; the different national situations are in some ways linear (or non linear !?..) combinations of these canonical models.

Historically, the French model of engineering education has been conceived as a political will to establish a severe education system for satisfying some national specific needs. The first Engineering Schools -the so-called and well known Grandes Ecoles- appeared at the middle of the 18th Century with the creation of the Ecole Royale des Ponts et Chaussées (1747) and the Ecole Royale du Génie (1748).

The canonical French model (today split into various sub-models) is caracterized by a kind of finalization of the formation system in relation with the national needs of the State and then of industry. When a new need for specific engineers appeared, one decided to create a new institution of engineering education. This model gives priority to the needs defined by the State or by big companies. It is also based on a particular and positive image of the engineer in the French society. The engineer plays in French an important economical, sociological and also political role. He or she is often at the top level of the hierarchy of professional values.

The engineer is certainly in France, more a manager (manager of technics, technologies or projects) than a technician. The selection of future engineers when entering the Grandes Ecoles and the elitism of these engineering schools are consequences of this socio-cultural determination. The curious result of the trend is that University did not appeared, historically, as an appropriated channel for educating these engineers. The principle "one specific need, one specific educational solution" leads to the multiplication of the Grandes Ecoles (180 Grandes Ecoles are officially recognized for delivering a national Diplom of Engineer in 1990). As a consequence, these Grandes Ecoles are very small units and can be described as small or medium educational entreprises, largely independant from the classical university system.

182

One knows also in France the important role played by the alumni associations, -Associations d'Anciens Elèves d'Ecoles d'Ingénieurs-. The placement of engineering students for well-paid jobs, the defense of the "corporation", the political influence, etc... are testimonies of the power of these institutions.

But it is amazing to observe that if on the one hand it exists a very strong educational system for the formation of engineers, on the other hand there is no regulation, no registration for practising engineering activities. There is no engineers'order in France, no engineering institutions as they exist in the United Kingdom. French engineers consider the origin of their formation as more important than the appurtenance to an engineering institution.

The german canonical model -that of the Technische Hochschulen or the Technische Universitäten-, can be compared with the French one, especially if one considers the very high level of academical qualification of the german engineers. But the German model differs from the French model, through the emphasis put on science and research, which are considered since a long time in Germany as an essential value in the society. At the beginning of the 19th Century, under the influence of the well-known politician and scientist Wilhem Von Humboldt, are founded some scientific institutions which try to establish a link between research and education and which develop their activities in an autonomous way : indépendance from the State power and from the industry influence -In other words, the historical canonical German model considers the engineer'formation as the result of an autonomous and specific development of science. Engineering education cannot be envisaged outside a very high scientific environment. The length of the contact with science is essential for the qualification of the engineer and one can observe in Germany a general trend for long studies (in principle 9 to 10 semesters after the secondary education, but often 13 to 15 semesters). Today, German engineering education -according to the historical or canonical model- is provided by some 15 big technical universities (West-Germany).

As in France, there is no obligatory registration for engineers and there is no regulation concerning engineering activities. Nevertheless the German engineers'institution -VDI, Verein Deutsche Ingenieure- plays an important role for promoting engineering activities, and for up-dating the engineers knowledges.

The third and main canonical model, the British one is, in some way, better known. It fundamentaly stands in opposition of the French and German models through a total inversion of the engineer "problematics". The engineer is more considered through his or her appurtenance to an Institution than through the education he or she received. The professional dimension of the British Engineering Institutions has a strong influence on the qualification of the engineers, especially through the accreditation and certification rules, but also through many procedures related to the regulation of professional practices, to the personal insurance and to the development of contiuning

education courses or seminars. But if the Institution of Civil
Engineers was founded very early in the 19th Century (1818),
the first structured academical engineering courses only appeared at the middle of the century (that is to say one century
after the first French Grandes Ecoles and 50 years after the
german technical universities). According to the British canonical model, the academical component of the engineer'formation
is one of the shortest within Europe and puts emphasis on the
technical and technological dimensions of the professional skill
of the engineer.

One can easily understand that an European engineer cannot
exist without a minimum of mutual recognition and understanding
of the cultural and historical basis.

NEW CONCERNS AND RECENT DEVELOPMENTS

During the 20 or 30 last years new needs for other engineers
appeared and new trends can now be observed that seriously
modify the historical canonical models.

First of all, one can mention contiuning education which is
a concern that emerged after 1968 -even if, historically original approaches have been developped in the past as for instance
with the creation of the Conservatoire National des Arts et
Métiers in France in 1794.

Since 1971 in France, a well-known law sets up a financial
system for continuing education. Engineering schools, as well
as the Engineer's Associations propose today many courses for
practising engineers and some of these courses allow individuals
to get a true Engineer Diplom or Degree. One can also observe an
increasing development of engineering continuing education in
the world (see for instance the "World Conferences on Continuing
Engineering Education").

In 1990, one can notice that continuing engineering education is beginning to change the view on what means "engineering
formation".

The second and important evolution, that appeared at the
beginning of the seventies is the creation and the development
of new engineering courses more oriented towards the production
world and more technologically oriented. With the Polytechnics
in Great Britain, with the german Fach Hochschule or also with
the French Instituts Universitaires de Technologie (IUT) that
all appeared about 1965-1970, a new approach of engineering
education is proposed in complement of the traditional way of
educating engineers. In 1990, two thirds of the german engineers
are graduating from the Fach Hochschulen. The success of this
new kind of educational system is bvious. A true "dual" (or
dualist) system of engineering education exists in many European
countries : long or higher education oriented towards design,
research and/or management on the one hand, shorter and production oriented education on the other hand.

But, of course, this dual or dualist system does not sim-
plify the search of European harmonization or convergency for
engineering courses, diplomas, degrees and titles.

A third trend progressively appears, which consists in the
development of post-graduate complementary courses for engineers. Thus in France, for instance, are proposed many specialized courses -DEA, DESS or again "MASTERES"-. The basic concept
behind this evolution refers to a double qualification of the
engineer : a first or initial education consisting in a classical Diplom of Engineer, followed by a short, specialized and
complementary course which allows a kind of adaptation to the
first job. These post-graduate courses are now largely offered
on the European formation market. They certainly will facilitate
the European mobility of engineers, disciplinary mobility as
well as geographical mobility.

During the 20 last years, one saw also an impressive deve-
loppement of research activities within technical universities
and engineering schools. This fourth evolution is very important for the post-industrial society and technology. The
impregnation of engineering education by research becomes more
and more a political objective. New channels or routes for
engineering education are propose which include basic research
activities.("formation through research").

Lastly, one could mention for the 15 or 20 last years a
radical transformation of the context of engineering education.
The international overture, the European cooperation become
the main key-word for higher education, especially for engineering education. This means a strong development of foreign
languages learning, of students and staff exchanges, of mutual
recognition of diplomas and degrees and sometimes of joint
courses or joint curriculum. The transferability of credits
within European higher education networks as well as the
delivery of "double" diplomas or degrees are testimonies of
this trend.

AND WHAT'S FOR THE FUTURE ?
It is often difficult to propose prospective tendencies
but considering engineering education and training, especially
within Europe, it could be useful to ask some questions that
could be answered in different ways by those responsibles of
the formation of future engineers.

1. Uniquity or multiplicity ?
A unique European engineer or multiple European engineers ?
This apparently obvious and over-simple question is linked with
an important debate concerning the fundamental aim of the European construction : have we to move towards an harmonized,
unified Europe, which erases all national particularisms or
have we to find a kind of co-existence of particular systems
which could me more and more compatible ?

This basic question "Uniquity or multiplicity ?" generates
others : is it necessary to define and introduce rules for the
the harmonization or unification of the only academical component of the engineer'formation or do we have to consider the
whole process of education training and professional development
of the engineer ? The "final product" taken into account by

THE FUTURE

FEANI for the EUR-ING title is a unique one or could it be
multiple ? If one agrees to find a good and balanced solution
between uniquity and multiplicity, could this European complex
model be exported to other continents or in other words, could
this European system be competitive compared with the American
or Janapese models of engineering education ? And what's about
its influence on engineering education within developing
countries ?

## 2. Functional differentiation

The second main question refers to the debate on the dual
or dualist approach on engineering education. If during more
than two centuries, the emphasis was put on the "highest" models
of engineering education, the recent development of a new kind
of "applied engineering education" (Fachhhochschule, Ecoles
techniques, Colleges and Polytechnics,...) introduces a new and
important concept which is the functional differentiation of
engineering education systems. One could more and more
prepare engineers either for design, for production, for
research or for management. The engineer is no more determined
by his or her only disciplinary field, but perhaps more and more
by his or her professional profile or "style".

In which way, the European efforts for convergency and
compatibility will stress this functional differentiation or
will erase it ?

## 3. Towards a minimal European threshold

Ascertaining the multiplicity of European educational
systems and the positive consequences of this diversity, a
third question is related to the minimal and common threshold
that one has to consider for the recognition of the different
engineering educational programme.

Is it possible for instance to define such a minimal threshold under which level no offical recognition is acceptable ?
If one considers the only academical dimension of problem, will
this threshold be a certain length of the studies ? Many
European specialists consider now a four year course as a
minimum for allowing the engineer to adapt his or her career
to different evolutions. Another possibility could be to consider this threshold in terms of educational content or curriculum
as for example a programme including a strong scientific basis,
a technical and technological initiation, an overture to economy
and management and the development of communication skills (including foreign languages mastery).

At the present day, the discussion on such a commun and
basic education or such an European threshold seems to be not so
far advanced.

## 4. Engineers, technicians and other professional staff

The European debates show how it is difficult to consider
the only engineer. If one takes into account the recent developments of the modern industry, it seems to be more and more clear
that thinking about engineering education without considering
the globality of the system of education of many professionals

186

at different levels can be dangerous for the competitivity of
enterprises in the future.

The problem is no more to isolate engineers and to define
the best way for the education ánal training of engineers only,
but it is perhaps more important to better integrate, the
formation of engineers, technicians, economists and other
professionals. The competitivity depénds more and more of the
capabilities of well educated and training multidisciplinary
teams or groups.

Thus the future will certainly show more continuity and
complementary between the various sub-systems of education and
training of professionals.

## 5. European yes indeed, but in what European ?

What will caracterize the future European engineer ? In
what the British, French or German engineer will be considered
as a fully European engineer ?

In some way for instance the FEANI  EUR. ING Title does not
include any specific requirements and does not really distinguish "national" and "European" engineers.

Is it necessary to consider the foreign languages learning
and mastery as an obligation ? The French "Commission des Titres
d'Ingénieurs" and "Conference des Grandes Ecoles" decide for
instance some years ago to incite the various Grandes Ecoles
to include the teaching of two foreign languages in the engineer's curriculum.

Is it also necessary to impose a minimum of 4 to 6 months
of study abroad, for any future European engineer ?

## 6. National, European or... Americain or world wide accredition

For a better European transparency and a better mutual
information about existing engineer's formations, is it necessary to establish a kind of European accredition Board ? What
will be the future of the various national bodies that provide
accredition or certification ?

This question leads to the problem of the compatibility of
such an European accredition system with the existing American
one -the Accredition Board of Engineering and Technology,
ABET- and also with what is done in Japon, in the South East
Asia or in Australia and New Zealand.

## CONCLUSION

Engineering education and training cannot be defined without
understanding the actual and complex needs for more qualified
engineers and their various specific contexts.

Industrialists, journalists and other professionals take more
and more part to the discussion about the formation of engineers.
The recruitment of engineering students and the creation of
links between various educational sub-systems ("higher" engineer, production engineer, technician,...) are, for instance,
some of the questions which are now often asked in many official
conferences and forum.

## THE FUTURE

In other words, the formation of engineers is linked with a society debate which concerns not only engineers but also many other professionals. In some way, the European cooperation helps to force engineers as well as educationists, industrialists or politicians to work together and to find new solutions which should be an acceptable compromise between the respect of traditional roots and the anticipation of more complex and international needs.

# 15. Putting the UK in its European context

D. WHITTLETON, Ove Arup & Partners

## Synopsis

This paper looks at a sample of European countries and examines some of the legal, professional, practical and cultural considerations which affect the practice of a consulting Engineer. Some conclusions are drawn concerning the approaches which may be required to operate successfully in this new environment.

## Introduction

1.    The implications and effects of the open market are examined from the viewpoint of a multinational, but UK-based, professional Engineering consultancy.    It is indicative of the diversity of operational and cultural differences, which defy generalisations about the new approaches we need to adopt.  What we will seek to do, therefore, is to examine in a little detail the way things work in a few of the other European countries, with a view to drawing some useful conclusions - which would apply equally to our European competitors looking at the United Kingdom as a potential market.

## Putting the UK in its Euro-context

2.    Working in a Europe unbounded by national barriers is not going to be the free market doddle many observers would have us believe.    Throughout this paper both brickbats and bouquets will be delivered in almost equal measure, without nationalistic fear or favour.    We shall be publicly holding up for scrutiny France, Germany, Spain and Portugal,  and taking a look at the formalities of practising within the wider European context;    the operational and practical considerations of business dealings between these countries; and the cultural differences that will be encountered, in

spite of "Euro-Glasnost".

3. According to a recent poll in the "Economist", France has the most impressive credentials in commitment to the European Economic Community. On a scale of 1 (high) to 10 (low), France ranked top, Spain came 3rd, Germany came 6th, Britain came equal 9th (with Greece) and Portugal came equal 11th (with Italy).

4. While we in the UK appear to score well on commitment to the single market, we flounder on future integration and the European ideal.

**Fig. 1    The best Europeans**  (Extract from "The Economist" 23 June 1990)

|  | Implementation of 1992 Measures | State aid to Industry | Total (max 60) | Rank |
|---|---|---|---|---|
| France | 7 | 5 | 39 | 1 |
| Spain | 4 | 4 | 36 | =3 |
| West Germany | 8 | 5 | 35 | 6 |
| Britain | 9 | 8 | 31 | =9 |
| Portugal | 2 | 4 | 28 | =11 |

### France - A Thumbnail Portrait

5. Although separated by only 20 miles of water, hundreds of years of shared fortunes and an 80-year alliance have done little to diminish the differences between France and the UK and our construction industries reflect this. Though a French construction project may superficially resemble a British one, the ways it is planned, financed, procured and executed can be very different.

6. One of the things most striking to the British professional is the dominance of the Engineer in France, and the less obvious distinctions between professional and commercial relationships. Over and above this is the greater integration of building with civil Engineering.

7. The Engineer from one of the *grandes ecoles* enjoys an influential and prestigious position and this in turn ensures that the general level of competence of qualified Engineers

is high.  Engineers are involved in almost every aspect of
the design and management of construction projects.

8.  The French Engineer is more likely to be the employee of
a building contractor, or of a *bureau d'etudes*.  *Bureaux
d'etudes* (BET) are a feature of the French construction scene
but have no real British equivalent.  They come closest to
resembling a multi-disciplinary Engineering consultancy.

9.  By contrast with Engineers, Architects in France have a
lower public profile and they are usually poorly paid, though
their position is protected by legal statute. The role of the
French architect is limited to conceptual design and he
usually has little involvement in detailed design or
management, except for the public sector.  Only a registered
architect can apply for a *permis de construire*, the
equivalent of British building permissions.

10.  Educational qualifications are important and hold the
key to career development and social status.  Engineers have
an important role in France. An Engineering diploma from an
influential institution is a passport to the senior ranks of
government, the civil service, industry and business.

11.  Many of the matters which have to be dealt with in
British contracts are already covered by French National
laws.  Consequently, contracts tend to be shorter than in
Britain.  This, and a general tendency to rely on good
commercial ethics, rather than multiple clauses, helps to
ensure good performance from the Owner's point of view.

12.  Another practice which contributes to a French Owner's
satisfaction with the performance of construction than his
British counterpart is the existence of compulsory defects
insurance.  All parties to a contract, including the client,
must be insured against defects in the building and the
subsequent problems are dealt with in a similar fashion to
motor insurance claims in this country:  the repairs are
carried out at the insurance companies' expense and liability
is then debated in court. For the most part, this practice
insulates the client from the kind of equivocations over
responsibility that are a common feature in the UK.  The
Owner has the additional benefit of full reimbursement for
remedial works.  Although the insurance aspects are not
strictly part of the construction industry, it could be
interesting to observe whether the French approach to defects
liability can contribute to solving some of the problems
which UK industry faces.

13.  For British professional consultants hoping to make an
impact in France, there are several pointers to be aware of.
Though practices are beginning to change, the traditional

approach still holds sway in France, possibly because there is little evidence of Owner dissatisfaction with it.

14. UK professionals wishing to undertake business in France should demonstrate some competence in the French language, to which there is a strong patriotic commitment. Although the average French practitioner has a better command of English than most Britons have of French, he is often unwilling to speak English unless his UK counterpart has first shown his mettle in French! (Not unnaturally, this reluctance to use English does not present itself in quite so marked a form when the French practitioner is looking for business in the UK.)

15. Since most professional services in France are concentrated within *bureaux d'etudes* or within contracting organisations it could be difficult for the single-discipline British Engineering consultant to break into the French construction scene.

16. The role of British consultants in France may remain slightly peripheral, unless they can combine into a single entity to perform the role of *bureau d'etudes* for the Owner. The French would probably have an aversion to the concept of dealing with several British firms, as against one French firm. So quite clearly, British firms will have to adapt to offer something similar. The all-purpose *bureau d'etudes,* which offers both professionalism and commercialism could pose a threat to some of the less efficient, single-discipline, British Engineering consultants, project and construction managers.

### France: The Engineer - Status, Operational and Practical Considerations

17. Engineers normally appoint a team to see the work through the design and construction stages, consisting of an Engineer, an architect and whatever other specialists are necessary. (See Fig. 2)

18. In France, the Engineer is the dominant construction industry professional, heavily involved in design, in Engineering consultancy and in *bureaux d'etudes.* Many of the functions which, in the UK, would be performed by building or quantity surveyors are performed by an Engineer. He also supervises work on site for the client and for contractors and has a key role in the management hierarchy of contracting companies.

19. Day-to-day practice has seen the tacitly-accepted evolution of two grades of qualified Engineer: those who

192

## Fig. 2 France - Relations between Functions and Participants

(Extract from CIRIA Special Publication 66)

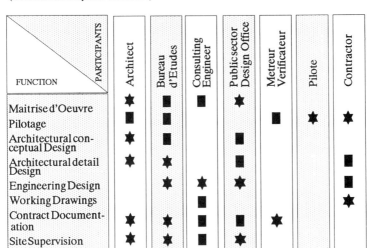

| FUNCTION \ PARTICIPANTS | Architect | Bureau d'Etudes | Consulting Engineer | Public sector Design Office | Metreur Verificateur | Pilote | Contractor |
|---|---|---|---|---|---|---|---|
| Maitrise d'Oeuvre | ★ | ■ | ■ | ★ | | | |
| Pilotage | ■ | ■ | | | ■ | ★ | ★ |
| Architectural conceptual Design | ★ | ■ | | ■ | | | |
| Architectural detail Design | ★ | ★ | | ■ | | | ■ |
| Engineering Design | | ★ | ★ | ★ | | | ■ |
| Working Drawings | | ■ | | | | | ★ |
| Contract Documentation | ★ | ★ | ■ | ■ | ★ | | |
| Site Supervision | ★ | ★ | ■ | ★ | | | |
| Cost Control | ■ | ■ | | ★ | ★ | | |

★ Frequently    ■ Occasionally

have been educated in the *grandes ecoles* and those who have qualified by another route. Graduates of the *grandes ecoles* tend to be the seed-corn of senior management in all areas; Engineers from the latter stratum work on sites, on detailed drawings and the like. It is possible, though difficult, to graduate from the drawings/site level to the senior management level. French Engineers are well trained and high calibre. Because of their involvement in all aspects of the building and civil Engineering construction process, it is difficult for others to break into the system.

20. The UK Engineer also enjoys an excellent reputation and probably has an advantage in dealing with more open-ended problems. For example, UK Engineers are reputedly better at feasibility studies than the French. A few UK consulting Engineers are practising in France, but they work mainly for British or international clients. Some have also undertaken work for French clients, but French Architects, particularly, suffer a fair degree of pique when prestigious projects go to foreigners.

21. The term "Engineer" is not a protected title in France and in the construction industry the practice of merely adopting the title without having the formal qualifications is widespread and much abused.

## Germany - Overview

22.   The prime result of the collapse of border controls
between East and West is likely to be an enhancement of the
role the GDR, its industries and its systems will play in the
Europe of 1992 and beyond.  In terms of commercial structure,
however, the West German model is likely to prevail.

23.   As far as construction is concerned there are eleven
different West Germanies, or *Lander,* each of which is
subdivided into communes.   Each of these in turn is a
corporate entity which makes its own decisions, especially in
building, town planning, local facilities, transport, etc.

24.   Consequently, all but the very largest building
contractors tend to concentrate their activities within the
*Land* or even the commune to which they belong.   British
contractors have few prospects in such a set-up unless they
undertake joint projects with German contractors who are
familiar with the local planning situation, the rules, the
availability of labour, etc.

25.   The UK Engineer or Architect must also accept that the
German Owner demands and is accorded high quality in his
projects, thanks to the quality of education and training
which professionals and artisans receive.   Whether Engineer,
Architect, Site Manager or Craftsman, all have a common
educational and training background and each understands the
other's   technical   problems.      Consequently,   competent
craftsmen can be relied on in a way that is not possible in
the UK.

26.   The other side of this idyll is embodied in the saying:
"In France everything is permitted; in England everything is
permitted  unless  it  is  expressly  forbidden;  in  Germany
everything is forbidden unless it is expressly permitted."
Germany has many apparent barriers to trade, simply because
of its formalised and well-established system of ensuring
compliance with the legal and technical requirements of trade
and industry.

27.   An  inherent  part  of  the  German  approach  is  its
protectionism.   The  terms  "Engineer"  and  "Architect"  are
legally protected.  Fee scales are enshrined by statute and
fee competition does not, theoretically at least, exist. And
this applies even at the trades level, where a German artisan
must be registered and must have passed the appropriate tests
and examinations in order to be accredited.

28.   The German construction industry does not suffer from
lack of capital, because the contractors are dominated by the
banks.   So tendering competition takes place on a rather

different risk basis from the UK. The funding is available and margins can be pared down. British contractors would be wise not to stray into competition within the German domestic market, unless they have the support of a joint venture with a German contractor.

29.  Despite these constraints, the British do possess certain strengths:

o  Private sector participation in otherwise public sector projects

o  Alternative methods of procurement which can help to guarantee completion dates

o  Improvements in the management of the construction process to cope with growing size and sophistication of projects

o  Cost control procedures throughout all stages of a project

30.  By contrast, the West German industry has progressed beyond or has advantages over UK in such areas as:

o  Its skilled and reliable workforce

o  Building professionals who are less narrowly specialised, with equal ability to those in the UK, and greater flexibility to adapt to new, high-tech demands

o  An aptitude for producing high quality engineered products such as kitchen fittings, curtain walling and windows

o  Development of new technology in construction applications

31.  The attentions of the West German construction industry towards moving into the UK market may now have been turned in the direction of the large new markets in Eastern Europe. But it would be unwise for UK practitioners to be complacent about competing or collaborating in these new areas of opportunity.

## Germany - The Formalities

32.  Consultancy is highly protected in Germany and although the consultant/contractor relationship is similar to that in the UK, the consultant's relationship with the Owner or

Client is much broader.

## Fig. 3     Germany - Normal Contractual Relationship
(Extract from "CIRIA Special Publication 68")

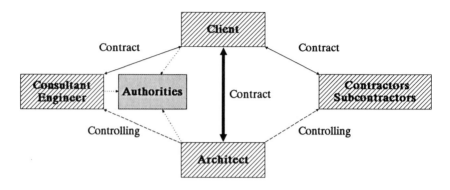

33. Fee competition is banned by national ordinance (HOAI - *Honarordnung fur Architekten and Ingeniure*). Attempts by large and powerful organisations to negotiate fees below the

## Fig. 4     Germany - HOAI Fee Scales in Percentage Terms
(Extract from "CIRIA Special Publication 68")

| Total Cost DM | Fee Zone I | Fee Zone III | Fee Zone V |
|---|---|---|---|
| 50,000 | 6.6% / 8.1% | 10.0% / 12.9% | 14.9% / 16.3% |
| 500,000 | 6.7% / 7.7% | 9.0% / 11.1% | 12.4% / 13.5% |
| 5,000,000 | 4.5% / 5.25% | 6.3% / 7.7% | 9.0% / 9.8% |
| 50,000,000 | 4.5% / 5.0% | 5.6% / 6.6% | 7.3% / 7.8% |

Fee Zone I = Simple Buildings (barracks, halls, simple agricultural buildings, etc.)

Fee Zone III = Dwelling Houses, primary schools, manufacturing buildings, etc.

Fee Zone V = Hospitals, specialist factory buildings, laboratories, concert buildings, etc.

minimum HOAI have been firmly quashed. However, clients do use the basic scales embodied in HOAI as a pick-and-mix bag to select those services they want. The fee is based upon total cost. Hence there is no real incentive to control cost overruns. These are quite common in Germany; +10% is usual, +50% not uncommon and even +100% not unknown. Germany has not cornered the market in cost overruns, of course.

## Germany - Operational and Practical Considerations

34.    The civil/structural engineering profession in West Germany has more cachet and is better paid than in the UK. However, UK firms enjoy a good deal of international respect because of their high standards and independence.

35.    M&E practitioners in West Germany do more of the detailed design work than their UK counterparts and, with the increasing importance of the services element in new construction projects, there could be opportunities for them in the UK.

36.    In many ways the Germans are the Japanese of Europe. They share many of the strengths and weaknesses which present both problems and opportunities and provide many valuable lessons for us.    Like Japan, Germany can show the UK the benefits of an efficient system of standards, consistently applied; of emphasising quality and of investing in and believing in education and training.    Hence their average performance is probably better than in the UK.    The British may have flair, individuality and some world-class managers and designers, but we need to strive to build markets while the markets are there.

## Spain - Overview

37. Spain is the fastest-growing economy in the EC and is described as the California of Europe. It has rapidly-growing inward investment and massive infrastructure programmes.

38. There is as yet very little penetration of the Spanish construction market by foreign firms, except in tourist projects, but there has been a lot of acquisition interest from abroad, particularly France, as European firms try to enter the Spanish market. It is largely through European insurance companies and property developers investing in Spain that foreign contractors and professional firms could gain access to the market, as Spain herself lacks the finance to fund large programmes.

39. The professions, particularly architects, are highly protected in Spain. Each has its own college or professional

**Fig. 5   Spain - Team Relationships - Private Sector building project**

(Extract from "CIRIA Special Publication 67")

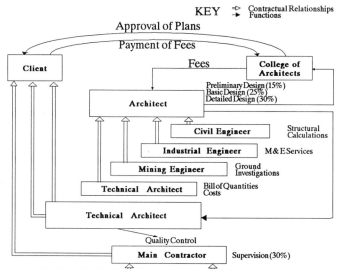

institution, to which by law all practitioners must belong. The law defines duties, practices and fee scales for both Architects and Engineers. There are few registered foreigners. New EC directives require mutual recognition, yet a number of complaints are being processed by the EC at the moment, but it will undoubtedly remain hard for foreign professionals to win work.

40.    There are many separate professions, all currently overmanned, which jealously guard their privileges and restrictive practices.    There are also strong contractors with powerful financial backing.    The complexity of relationships and the bureaucratic professional and legislative constraints - well-understood by Spanish consultants - coupled with tortuous foreign exchange procedures (which do not affect Spanish enterprises) mean that Spain will be a difficult market to break into for the foreseeable future.

41.    While Architects in Spain are powerful, carry the burden of liability in projects and are protected by their college, no such status applies to Engineers in engineering projects. Contractors have to be licensed and classified for public contracts on top of the complex series of registrations required by any other business enterprise in Spain.    Working in Spain is still difficult for foreign firms, although the single European market directives should make it progressively easier.

## Spain:   Operational and Practical Consideration

42.    As a general rule, there exists no legal requirement to use approved products and no import restriction on products which do not meet UNE *(Una Norma Española)* standards. Neither do existing insurance arrangements require the use of approved products.  Since product suppliers do not carry any legal liability for building defects, the use of approved products has no liability implications, except for the architect and technical architect.    However, many of the UNE standards for steel and concrete and for design and testing procedures are embodied in the obligatory NBE *(Normas basicas de la Edificaciòn)*.

43.    There is no obligation to carry insurance cover and some professionals who are not in independent practice or have low workloads do not bother to insure.

## PORTUGAL: An Overview

44. Portugal, with 15% of the population of the UK, has about 2.5% of the construction activity. However, its growth rate is high and it is scheduled to receive a high proportion of EC funding. When that happens, its main problem will be to find and manage enough projects to absorb the funds it could draw on and this could provide an opportunity for British contractors and consultants.

45. Its industry is less tightly-controlled than Spain's. Building regulations in the past have been slack but much tighter control on planning and standards is now being applied, particularly in the tourist areas, where building had got out of control.

46. The professions are not regulated to the extent they are in Spain. There is an Association of Architects and an Association of Graduate Engineers, with which Architects and engineers must be registered if they practise in Portugal.

47. Unlike Spain, the Engineers are the dominant profession. Architects are not involved in supervision and their role usually ends with planning permission. Detailed design is usually done by contractors and for large projects, a team of engineers is appointed as *fiscals* for the project and cost control, performing some of the tasks of a quantity surveyor.

48. Overall, the quality of building is variable. Building for the up-market commercial sector is very good and the liabilities attaching to the contractor generally ensure a reasonable standard, but the lack of regulation of 'black economy' housing means that this is of lower quality. Quality also tends to decline during panic development, as has applied in the Algarve.

49. In some ways, the less rigid and protectionist system of Portugal makes it easier for UK professionals and contractors to work there than in Spain. Nonetheless, in both countries the legal system is very different from the UK and the bureaucratic procedures involved in running a business and in obtaining permissions are slower and much more difficult.

## Portugal: Operational and Practical Considerations

50. According to the nature of the project - Small, Large or Tourist - so different planning procedures prevail.

**Fig. 6 Procedures for obtaining a** *Licenciamento Municipal de Obras particulares* (Extract from "CIRIA Special Publication 67")

### SMALL PROJECTS PROCEDURE

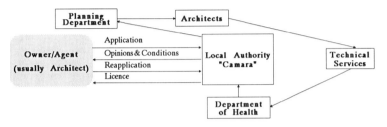

### LARGE PROJECTS PROCEDURE

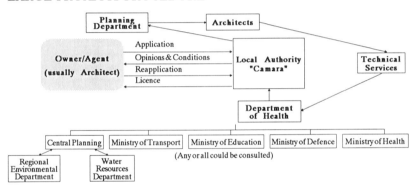

### TOURIST PROJECTS PROCEDURE

51. In practice there are no product standards of Portuguese origin. The standards of nearly all of the countries of the EC, as well as international standards are accepted by the Portuguese and are then translated into Portuguese.

52. However, the majority of designers and builders are not

familar with all the different types of standards and this
creates a situation in which designers are unable to make
categorical specifications of products. They tend, therefore
to specify a given product 'or equivalent'. This is a
problem which Portugal will soon have to address, because it
has led to an influx of low-quality materials from other
countries where the materials would not have met national
standards, and because EC-wide standards will eventually
require that Portugal organise itself better.

53. Because price is the prime concern of the Portuguese
Owner, quality is sacrificed, both by the Owner and hence by
the manufacturer. Speculation is rife, for example, that
'off-spec' products and substandard materials from Spanish
manufacturers find a ready market in Portugal.


**Portugal: Status Comparisons**

54. EC Architects wishing to practise in Portugal may do so
if they hold qualifications recognised by the EC Architects'
Directive (85/384.)

55. While the strength of the Portuguese architectural
profession is growing, having been overshadowed by the large
number of Engineers (about 15:1), Engineers still form the
dominant profession. Engineers form about 30 percent of
members of the parliament and are usually to be found in key
administrative positions in government and private industry.
This makes the profession highly influential and a popular
career choice.

56. Engineers design and quantify contracts, administer and
co-ordinate a project. Many Portuguese engineers are
employed as site engineers and are legally responsible for
the erection of buildings as project managers and/or as
administrative staff. As there are large numbers of building
companies, these engineers tend to move from one company to
another and contractors have to pay higher prices to recruit
them.

57. There are about five large firms of multi-discipline
consulting engineers with more than 200 employees. The rest
are very small.

58. The basic difference in training between UK and
Portuguese engineers is that in Portugal the education is
more broadly based and, consequently, engineers take on a
more managerial role.

59. When a foreign Engineer wishes to work in Portugal, the
Ministry of Education liaises with the university at which

he/she qualified, in order to recognise their diplomas.

60.   The indications are that the potential market for
consulting engineers is in the field of project management.
Consequently, firms may be orientating their services towards
this, away from detailed design.   Portugese engineers are
paid about 60 percent of UK, 50 percent of French and 45
percent of German fees, which makes them very competitive in
the EC marketplace.

## Portugal:   Activities of Foreign Firms

61.   It has been suggested that in certain areas of
industrial design (e.g. industrial effluent treatment) the
market has been rather too small for Portuguese consulting
engineers to develop their design capabilities.   This may
well create opportunities for engineers from other countries
in the EC to work in association with Portuguese firms.

62.   Since its accession to the EC, Portugal has been
eligible for EC structural funds and the effect of the
increased funding on the construction will therefore be
enormous and will present huge opportunities for foreign
firms.

63.   Generally, the reaction of Portuguese contractors to the
influx of foreign firms has been to welcome them, since joint
ventures have often meant increased opportunities in their
own market.   It is not likely that Portuguese contractors
will be able to offer fierce competition for work in other
areas of the EC, since even the largest firm only has 120
employees in Europe.

64.   Some engineering consultants regard their low fees as a
1992 trump card.   Once the current construction boom is over
in Portugal in about 1995, Portuguese Engineers will have to
start casting around to survive.

65.   The Portuguese people are generally very well disposed
towards British Business and it is much easier to get by
without knowing the Portuguese language than it is in Spain
without fluent Spanish.   However, for longer term business
links, the professional will need to speak Portuguese.

## Discussion

66.   We have examined a sample of European countries, and
looked at some of the legal, professional, practical and
cultural considerations which affect the construction
industries in those countries.   Along the way, we have

compared the British industry and so have an impression of
five member states.

67.   However sucessful the implementation of the single
Market and however seriously the various EC directives are
taken, there is no doubt that for a long time to come,
construction and the professions which go with it, will be a
locally centred activity.   Exporting a manufactured product
and ensuring compliance with national or pan-European
standards is one thing; exporting services into an
environment steeped in history, tradition, local practices,
etc. is quite another.   For this reason, those in the
construction industry, wherever their base, will have to be
selective and gear up seriously for individual markets; it
will not be possible for a firm to take a few strategic steps
and then announce that it is ready for Europe.

68.   Nevertheless, some general observations are possible.

69.   Consultancies need to look carefully at the kind of work
they do, or wish to do, and then consider what it is they are
offering in their chosen markets. This may sound like a
statement of the obvious, but the scope of service - what
level' of detail, duration of involvement, etc. - is so
variable between (and within) markets that it is possible to
get things hopelessly wrong, which in a competitive
environment can be quite disastrous.   One method of
overcoming these kinds of problems is to form collaborative
ventures with "local" firms - this enables both parties to
offer the skills they are best at, and ensures that the
service is attuned to local requirements, including the
comfort of the client or promoter.   There are signs that
activities of this kind are beginning to increase quite
rapidly.

70.   In terms of standards, as applied to professionals,
compliance with the EC Professional Qualifications Directive
89/48/EEC - adopted in 1988 and due in force on 4 January
1991 - should ensure basic competence of practising
individuals, although such Directives are (necessarily)
somewhat woolly and open to interpretation. They will not, of
course, guarantee a quality service from a professional firm.
As ever, performance, satisfied clients and reputation
generally will be the things that count in the long term.   In
the early days of a consulting firm's activities in a "new"
market, accurate definition of the service and very specific
briefing is the only way to guarantee a service which hits
the target.

71.   Engineering consultancies also need to remember that in
any market which is "opening up", be it national, European or
global, two-way traffic is being encouraged and is to be

expected.    Smaller firms offering a range of skills tailored
to a traditional local market will probably do better to look
at the "inward" flow of clients and/or projects, rather than
trying to export thier services.


REFERENCES

Fig. 1          Extract from the "Economist" 23 June 1990

Figs. 2-6       Extracts from "CIRIA Special Publications 66,
                67 and 68

                "European    Communities    Directives    -
                Construction."    List   and   Timetable   for
                Implementation at 18 July 1990.

# Discussion on Papers 13–15

A. LEGGATT, CEDIC, Farnham

In considering the future, it is helpful to state the basic elements of what we are doing. My reading of the elements of a construction project is as follows

Primary aim: The formulation and execution of a solution to a technical challenge.

Secondary aim: The use of an appropriate contractual and commercial framework to enable the technical solution to be completed expeditiously.

You may wish to use different wording, but I am sure you will agree that the aim of construction is to construct!

The subject matter of this conference has been entirely concerned with the secondary aim as stated above: this is not to say that the conference lacks importance, but in framing future secondary procedures we must bear in mind that their purpose is to facilitate the accomplishment of successful construction. Engineers and others engaged on the primary aim are not usually bothered with frontiers. Technical solutions do not vary much from one country to another. It is in the secondary operations that the barriers are found; in breaking down those barriers we must take care not to infringe the freedom of action found in the primary field.

Turning to calculation and training: Mr Michel has told us of the problems, and I know them well through my work on the drafting party for an Engineers' Directive: a party set up by the European Commission (DG III) and convened by FEANI. Our philosophical starting point in the FEANI drafting party has been the realization that, despite their very different educational systems for engineers, Spain does not seem to have any more bridge failures than Scotland, nor do France and Denmark etc. So the end product of these systems - the professional engineer - has a reassuring equivalence across the Community (indeed across the world). We are determined to find a method of equating the differing educational systems so that mutual

recognition of the status and value of professional
engineers can be achieved.

**J. A. ARMITT,** John Laing Construction Ltd, Hemel
Hempstead

I would like to thank Dr Caronna for his promises of
consultation, and expand on comments made yesterday as
to the extent of cross-border contracting in the EC.

It is true that the construction market is very
large, but also that it is based largely on local
business.  FIEC statistics show that 90% of contractors
employ fewer than ten people, and 95% employ fewer than
100 people.  In the UK, the largest 20 companies
account for about 20% of the market.  About 12 of these
companies are very active outside the UK.  A similar
pattern is found in France, Germany etc.

These same companies are most likely to show interest
in cross-border activity within the EC.  Bearing in
mind that they have shown no reluctance to pursue
opportunities thousands of miles away, with many
physical and contractual obstacles to success, why
should they not seek to compete in the EC countries?
The reasons have far more to do with the people than
with conditions of contract: local client contact,
understanding of local culture, local suppliers, labour
attitudes etc.  Even in the UK, for all but the largest
contracts we would not expect to be very successful in
seeking work 100-200 miles from the office.

In conclusion, I would suggest that the motivation
seems to be more for consumer protection and
potentially achieving advantages of different systems
than for single market competition.

**C. SOUTHCOMBE,** Polytechnic South West, Plymouth

I accept that the conference has been organized by
the Institution of Civil Engineers; however, the theme
is 'Construction without frontiers'.  In reviewing
education and training, the barrier between the
engineer and the architect has not been removed.
Yesterday, reference was made to the area of activity
of the engineer and architect in France and Germany,
and the comment of a delegate that a large proportion
of UK engineering graduates find employment in the
building industry.

It is very important to pull the professionals
together.  Academic institutions clearly need guidance
on ways forward in order to plan for the future.  If we
want to have relatively free movement of students
between countries, they need to have defined
recognition of the studies carried out.

In view of the diversity of study periods (3-6
years), are we being realistic in considering total or
virtually total commonality between educational courses?

H. A. ALLAN, Haiste International Ltd, Leeds
   I scanned the papers presented at this conference for
any reference to construction site safety.  Dr
Caronna's paper was the only one where the subject was
briefly mentioned.  Those of us who have worked
overseas are only too well aware that standards of site
safety in some countries are poor, indeed appalling in
certain cases.  This seems to result from a combination
of ignorance and attitude.  From personal experience I
regret to say that there are examples of unacceptably
low site safety standards within the EC.  Quite apart
from the moral issue, i.e. our responsibility as
professionals for the welfare of site operators and
others, there is the economic imbalance arising from
the variance in provision of site safety measures
between member states.   Are any steps being taken to
collect data from member states in a uniform manner so
as to highlight differences in levels of site safety?
Are there any proposals to establish minimum standards
and to ensure that legislation such as the UK Health
and Safety at Work Act applies uniformly across member
states?

M. J. ROBERTS, Department of Transport, London
   Calls for harmonization are not coming from
consultants or contractors at this conference, but
rather from those engaged in studying European systems,
who perhaps are interested in building something other
than construction works.
   It is feared that standardized systems will be forced
on people without taking account of the needs of all
sectors.  We must get the best that Europe has to
offer, not just standard systems.
   Complete freedom is not possible.  It is not possible
for clients to specify what they want, manufacturers to
use what they want, and contractors to use what they
want.

R. CARONNA, Paper 13
   All that Mr Armitt has said is quite correct, but I
think that he has forgotten to cite the 'local
legislation', which in our view represents a set of
obstacles to the plans of small and medium sized
construction businesses which extend their activities
to another country within the Community.
   Of course, one of the motives for our actions is
better protection for the eventual user of the
constructed 'product', but we cannot and we must not
set aside something that is part of the formation of
the Single Market in the construction sector.
   I thank Mr Allan for noting that in my paper I
indicate that an aim of the Commission is an increase
in the quality of construction in the Community.   This

objective will enable us to reach a compromise in the
search for a uniform guaranteed working lifetime across
all the countries of the Community.

To this end, we should ask ourselves the following
question: would it be better to have a building
guaranteed for many years, but whose quality is poor;
or a building of high quality guaranteed for a period
acceptable in all countries?  I think the answer is
obvious.

# Closing address

T. M. RIDLEY, Imperial College

It is very difficult in a short presentation to give
an overview and sum up the essence of this conference
but let me first congratulate the Institution and the
speakers on bringing together so many excellent and
comprehensive papers on this important subject. Some
have stuck closer to the theme of the Community than
others, but all have been interesting. We have heard a
great deal about 'culture'.

Yesterday President Severn spoke of technical,
professional, financial, and cultural/social aspects of
the subject. All have come up during our discussion.
Foster gave an important and wide-ranging review of the
situation in the construction industry. He praised the
performance of the last decade but gave a rather gloomy
view of problems ahead if strategic actions are not
taken by firms.

Armitt later appeared to contradict this gloomy view
in an up-beat statement about the industry. He did
concur however that a problem existed because of the
low capitalization of UK firms and the nature of their
shareholding. Thus it seems to me that the future
depends on vigorous action by the industry itself but
also on the climate within which it is operating. I
hope that those people in the City who are examining
the charge of 'short-termism' will include the
construction industry in that examination.

Foster among many others stressed the need to reduce
confrontation between the parties. He spoke of the
importance of the growth of the number and size of
private sector, as opposed to public sector, clients.
He emphasized the market opportunities on the Continent
in various infrastructure projects, including
transport. Foster deplored the length of the
pre-construction period. I can only agree, having had
the good fortune to take the Tyne and Wear Metro from a
line on a map to digging tunnels in just three years,
and the Docklands Light Railway through planning,
design, building and operation while the East London
River Crossing was still in Public Inquiry.

Foster believed that single-point responsibility for

projects will be increasingly likely in the future. This I believe will have a major impact on education and training, though I was taken aback when Armitt appeared to say that arts graduates were being trained for managerial positions but that civil engineers were too busy with their specialist tasks to be so trained. As a new recruit to the education industry, I am turning my attention to the education of our industry leaders for the years 2010 to 2030 and beyond; whatever the conclusion I am convinced that it will be very different from the past. The 'rounded man' is a term for us to bear in mind, though I prefer the 'rounded engineer' to the rounded Oxbridge arts graduate!

Barnes gave us a clear exposition on the question of risk. Everyone worries about it. It has be deviled attempts to develop new approaches to public/private funding partnerships. Yet too few people understand it. I should certainly like to make the study of probability theory a fundamental part of the education of every lawyer as well as every engineer. Barnes also stressed the fundamental importance of the shrinking or minimization of risk, as well as, or even more importantly than, allocating risk.

We have heard much about 'teamwork' at the conference. I am sure that teamwork is essential between the parties as well as within each of the parties. I would commend the practice of putting a notice on the wall of every major participant in an engineering contract with the message 'We either succeed together or we fail together'. Barnes also made the important point that attitudes to risk must be integrated into the development of good management practices.

Ferry gave a comprehensive review of procurement and the differences in practice in a number of European countries. Harmonization he believes will be slow, a point echoed by a number of speakers on a variety of topics. In these circumstances, it seems to me that what is essential is that all managers should clearly understand differences between practices before we try to harmonize. As Barnes reminded us, issues are common, even though they underlie differing practices. Too often in this life we argue about detail and competing solutions to problems before we have agreed what the issues are.

Lalaurie and Haensel next gave us descriptions of the approaches to project organization in France and Germany. In France the differences between projects in the public and private sectors were emphasized, while we were given a clear statement of the legal basis for planning and construction in Germany. It was also interesting to have presentations on construction management and control by Armitt and Pehuet. They know and understand each other's approaches because they are working together in an existing joint venture. Armitt described his management of labour, plant and materials and the increasing specialization of people and suppliers. Pehuet did not see the differences between France and the UK which are frequently cited. He stressed the fundamental importance and responsibility of the site manager; he too stressed that people are the most important asset. This, I believe, is of increasing and urgent importance given the demographic trends we are facing. We did have a discussion on the nature of construction projects. They were not like car production but rather like heavy engineering, in that there is no prototype. However, it is nonetheless necessary to design and develop a project from the beginning with regard to how it is to be built. The professional divisions within the industry often militate against this and there seemed to be general agreement that if you can control the design then you can control the cost.

We heard comprehensive papers by Craig (on finance, financial controls, cost audit and cash flow), and by Van Houtte, who from her position as an international lawyer highlighted the impact of Community rules and directives on existing liabilities and contractual arrangements. Bunni and Schneider covered insurance and dispute resolution. Bunni detailed the risk issues underlying insurance and the various items which may be insured in construction. Schneider compared different approaches to disputes in several countries, and gave a particularly lengthy and helpful list of references.

Craig spoke about case studies of risk and mentioned the Advanced Gas Reactors, the Thames Barrier and the Channel Tunnel. She referred to misjudging human behaviour; I think that this is tremendously important. It would seem important to me, while we are teaching probability theory to lawyers, that we also acquaint engineers with psychology and group dynamics. She also said 'high prizes can be won if the senior management of the supplier and the purchaser are pulling in the same direction'. Shades of 'succeed together or fail together'. I do strongly urge that the Channel Tunnel be used as a case study for the future. Unique though it is, there are many lessons to be learned.

In spite of the triumph of Transmanche Link tunnelling to date, there is still along way to go. However, it does not seem sensible to allow, or indeed require, promoters to revert to their roles as bankers and contractors, and to create a new owner organization with no track record. Nor is it sensible to unite them, or disunite them, with one of the most divisive contracts that the world has seen. On top of this the bankers can turn off, or threaten to turn off, the cash

flow at regular intervals. I do not know what your
relations with your bank manager are like, but I can
tell you that to have 200 bank managers is no laughing
matter. What I would finally say about the project, in
the context of this conference, is that any problems
between the cultures of France and Britain are
relatively insignificant compared with those between
Eurotunnel and TML. Incidentally, I do deplore the
tendency of some speakers at the conference to refer to
Europe rather than the Continent where they are making
comparisons with the UK.

Caronna very helpfully came and gave us a Commission
view. He reminded us of the size of the European
construction industry, and listed and described some of
the most important relevant directives. He stressed the
need for minimum but uniform regulation and listed the
objectives of the second stage of the Commission's
study of the various legal systems in different
countries. He ended with a plea for the end to national
prejudices; not all of the delegates accepted his
views. Michel followed many others by emphasizing the
differing education and training practices in various
countries and again attributed this to cultural
differences. He compared the French, German and British
models and the existence, or not, of professional
registration. We are all nevertheless concerned with
continuing education and making engineers more
international. It is now possible for engineers from
Imperial College to spend the third year of their
four-year undergraduate degree studying in Paris. Lee,
speaking for Whittleton, spoke from the point of view
of the engineering consultant and said that while we
are still some distance from a Single Market, we are
slowly moving towards it. Leggatt, interestingly, said
that we may have been talking about the wrong issues.

I am not going to be tempted to answer Christopher
Foster; I shall leave you to provide your own answers.
I would simply say that I found the conference to be
have been very valuable, and that we are moving
together but at a speed which is far from clear. We do
need to stand back from masses of detail and strive for
mutual understanding of what is common between us and
what is  different - and to understand the underlying
issues and the nature of the product.

In other words we should concentrate on seeing the
wood for the trees and, if I may return to education,
we should ensure that our young people understand the
essential issues which relate to construction across
the Community. The only advice I can offer in closing
is to urge that we increasingly think as Europeans,
which we now are, but also to remember that we are
engineers engaged in the construction industry, which
by definition must be very practical.